W9-AJK-928

Celtic

Fables, Legends, and Folklore

John Hickey

Martin Hintz

Publications International, Ltd.

John Hickey is the business manager and national advertising sales director for *The Irish American Post*, an internationally distributed news magazine focusing on Irish and Irish American politics, culture, business, and sports. Hickey studied in Dublin and is a graduate of the London International Film School. He has also been the publisher of his own small press, featuring some of the Midwest's most prominent poets. Hickey is the coauthor of *Irish Wit and Wisdom.*

Martin Hintz is the publisher of the Milwaukee-based *The Irish American Post* magazine. A long-time journalist, he has written more than sixty books, including *Irish Wit and Wisdom*, which he coauthored, *Celtic Myths and Legends,* and the *Irish Wit and Wisdom* perpetual calendar. For sixteen years Hintz was the promotions director of Milwaukee Irish Fest, one of the world's largest Irish cultural events.

Editorial assistance: John Gleeson.

Publications International, Ltd., has made every effort to locate the owners of all copyrighted material to obtain permission to use the selections that appear in this book. Any errors or omissions are unintentional; corrections, if necessary, will be made in future editions.

Copyright © 2000 Publications International, Ltd. All rights reserved. This book may not be reproduced or quoted in whole or in part by any means whatsoever without written permission from:

Louis Weber, CEO
Publications International, Ltd.
7373 North Cicero Avenue
Lincolnwood, Illinois 60712

Permission is never granted for commercial purposes.

Manufactured in China.

8 7 6 5 4 3 2 1

ISBN: 0-7853-4108-0

Table of Contents

Introduction

The early Celts lived in a world of nature and spirit, of beautiful earthly things and some things not of this earth. It was a world where spirits and fairies ruled the night, and warriors and queens ruled the day. Seated around forest campfires or in the halls of the great kings, the ancient *seanachies* (Irish storytellers) were the historians of their age. They numbered among the highest members of the courts and were respected because of their wisdom and understanding of all things past, present, and—perhaps—even future.

Their stories kept the spirit of the Celts alive through the long, dusty ages: through wars, famine, conquests, colonialism, and now into modern life. For the Celts, their stories were educational missives, moral tales, highbrow narrations, epic adventures, stern warnings, marvelous tales, and—above all—fun and entertainment.

There is still a bit of the storyteller in most of the Irish, whose gift of gab is legendary. They have a marvelous tradition, wherein no one thinks twice about spending hours chatting, weaving words into wonderful tapestries, blending dreams, facts, and fancies into one.

For the Irish, there is nothing more impolite than a visitor not taking the time to hear a story. After all, the speaker is putting heart and soul into their words, which flow like the lovely Shannon toward the sea. The stories, songs, and poems in *Celtic Fables, Legends, and Folklore* draw on this rich heritage of the Irish, as well as on that of their Scottish and Welsh counterparts.

By giving full attention to these legends and myths, we learn how to conquer our own fears and rise to whatever the occasion merits. We become stronger, happier, and more confident in ourselves when we hear how Jack bested the devil, or how Finn McCool got one over on the Scottish giant. After all, if they can do it, why can't we?! This book of Celtic tales gives the reader a peek into the days of antiquity and then moves on to stories of the spirit world and Ireland's mythical landscape. For good measure, there's a bit o' sport included, some animal antics, several stories with religious twists, and—of course—some reflections on life, love, and death.

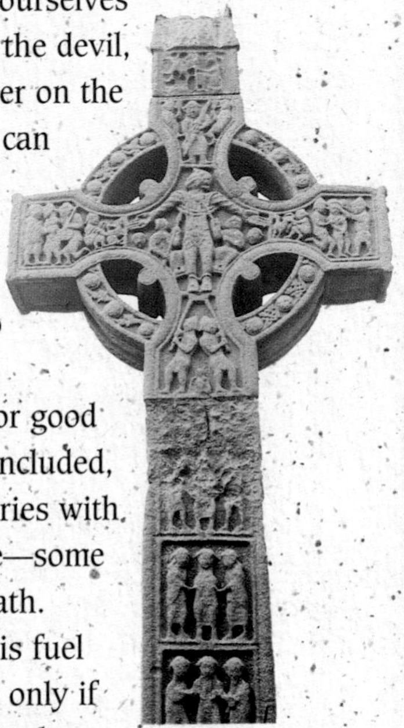

The vivid Celtic imagination is fuel for our own creative juices, but only if we allow ourselves to pass through an open door to this otherworld of words. So take the time to unlock the mystery of the Celtic soul, revel in the enjoyment of ancient tales, and learn that the use of one's imagination is a great antidote to "what ails ye."

Chapter One

Early Times

Three things one should do
every year—listen to
a storyteller at a fireside,
give a hand in a corn harvest field,
and climb an Irish mountain.

—*Michael John Murphy*, Mountain Year

Finn McCool and the Scots Giant

The great Irish warrior Finn McCool lived to be a middle-aged man without ever meeting his equal in sport or war. And for this, he was proud as a peacock. Finn had a great fortress in the Bog of Allen, and there he and his band of warriors would practice their swordplay and arrow shooting, or they would toss boulders 30 or 40 miles away, to build the quay off Dublin that we see today.

One day, poor Finn was quite depressed because his men were here and there, all wandering about, and he had no one to wrestle with or hurl or go a-hunting. So he was strolling about very long in the face, very lonesome in fact, when he spied a footman running swiftly across the dark bog. "Why the rush? What's blowing in the wind, young fellow?" asked Finn.

"It's the great Scots giant, Fear Rua, in the wind. He's come over the stones in the sea that lead from Scotland to Ireland.* He'll be here in less time than it takes the

**This refers to the Giant's Causeway, an extensive stretch of boulders off the far north coast of Ireland that legend says was a pathway for the ancients crossing the sea from island to island.*

stag to leap or the hare to run," came the reply. "Fear Rua wants to meet the great Finn McCool and see who is the best man."

"Woooo, waaaa," said Finn. "I hear that Fear Rua is three foot taller than me, and I'm three foot taller than any man in Ireland. I must find out more about how to deal with this fellow. I'll speak with Grainne about it all. She'll know what to do."

It wasn't far off or long about that the terrible Scotsman was seen walking with thunderous strides up the stony path that led across the bog to Finn's home. He carried a sword as sharp and long as three scythe blades and a spear the length of a house.

"Where is the man Finn McCool?" the giant roared when he reached the gates of the fortress. "Is he in?"

"He most certainly is not," said one of Finn's guards, looking at the giant from one of the corner towers of the fort. "He is hunting stags at Killarney. But there is someone within who will talk with you. Follow me, please." So off they went, the two of them. In the hall, the Scots giant spied the trunk of a long fir tree with an iron tip on it and a round block of wood with an iron, as wide as four chariot wheels.

"There is the shield and spear of Finn," said the guard. *Ubbabow!* thought the giant. *This Finn must be a great, strong fellow.*

They went into a room where sat the lady Grainne, calm as the full moon. Off in the corner was a cradle, with Finn tucked under the blankets as a young babe.

"You're welcome to sit, Fear Rua," Grainne said with a smile. "Relax by the fire, and have some supper." With that, she put down a big griddle cake, with the griddle itself inside—a round piece had been sliced from part of the rim. For a beefsteak, she gave him a piece of red oak planking, disguised with a thin layer of hard meat on the outside.

At the first bite of cake, the giant broke three of his teeth. When he tried to chew the beef, his remaining teeth stuck in the chewy wood.

"By me, ma'am," said the giant, extracting the splinters and pieces of oak from his mouth. "This is a strong diet you give your company."

"Oh, Lord love you," said Grainne. "The children here think nothing of it. She took the cake to where Finn was lying in the cradle and gave him the piece that had been removed earlier. With a great smacking of lips, Finn chewed up the cake. He gave Fear Rua a grand wink after it all went down. *Glory,* thought the giant. *These are wonderfully strong people.*

Well, Grainne couldn't let the giant go away without having a drink. So they laid a keg of beer in front of him, one that held four gallons, and the giant emptied it in one drink since he hadn't had any of the cake or meat.

"I'd like to see how Finn amuses himself after a meal," said the giant after draining the keg.

"That is fine," said the guard. "Step outside if all is well with you."

It was. And they did.

When they were outside, the guard pointed at piles of five large stones, each in the shape of a gatepost. "Those are their finger stones, the ones they cast to see who throws them the farthest. It is a great throw when one reaches Dublin. Sometimes, Finn does even better: He tosses them out into the sea where they stick upright."

The guard asked the Scots giant if he would like to try his hand at tossing the stones. The giant picked up

The Giant's Causeway in Northern Ireland

one stone and flung it as far and as hard as he could. The great rock barely made it to the bog when it came crashing down into the mud. There it was swallowed up with no sign of its passing. *That was a long way from either Dublin or the sea,* thought the Scots giant.

"You'll do better when you come to your full height," said the guard, looking up at the giant. "You can practice for a year or more with Finn, and then he'll suggest you play."

"Faith!" said the giant to himself. "To the underworld with Finn and his finger stones."

He asked the guard if there were any other ways that Finn and his men played. "Oh, yes," said the guard. "Finn and his fellows throw that handball over the house here. They run around and catch it before it lands on the turf. Every miss counts as one lost," said the smaller man. He pointed to a round rock that stood as tall as himself.

"Wonderful quare people are these Irish," Fear Rua marveled. "Maybe it wouldn't be a good idea for me to toss this stone over the house unless I practiced first by tossing it into air. My first try might miss and it would crash into the roof, disturbing the grand lady inside," he said, referring to Grainne, who was watching all this time from an open window. She waved at the giant for his consideration.

"So let me toss the stone into the air, to get the heft of it," said the giant. With a grunt, he picked up the boulder and threw it far into the sky. It returned to earth with a rush, hitting the giant square in the center of his head. The impact felled the giant, who awoke a few hours later, rubbing his head. He looked very angry.

"I suppose Finn won't be home tonight," he said to the guard, who had stood by the unconscious giant the whole time. "Sire, he'll be back in a week or more," the man replied.

"Well, bid my adieu to him. I must get back before the tide overtakes me on the crossing," the giant said, glad to be on his way. And he was never seen of again in the land of Finn McCool.

The Flight of the Sluggard

After a great meal was held at the fortress of Almhuin, the Fianna marched to Knockany in Limerick. There Finn McCool set up his tent and dispatched his warriors to search for game along all the lanes and byways, through the valleys and the mountains that straddle the rough borders of Limerick, Cork, and Kerry.

As he was sitting in his tent waiting for his men to return, Finn opened his chess board and began to play with one of his lieutenants, a man who was called Bald Conan. While they played, a scout approached to announce the arrival of a huge man dragging a broken-down horse after him. The man himself was lolling along, his feet going in all directions in a slow and witless manner.

When he was within hearing range, Finn said, "Who are you and what do you want?" The newcomer replied, "I am Giolla Deacair, the Slothful Fellow. That is the name I am called. The place I am from is not worthy of mention. No one will hire me, I'm so lazy. So I decided to come and talk with the Great Finn, seeking to be in his service."

And Finn replied, "Why should I hire such a person as you, who brings along such a sad-looking horse?"

The man rejoined, "The horse is for me. To carry me when I deliver messages, I am so lazy. Hire me, and you will never regret it."

This caused everyone around to shout with laughter, loud enough to frighten all the wild hares, seals, hawks, and whales, so that they fled far away to their lairs in the mountains, forests, or ocean.

Looking for more such humorous release, but still not believing he should employ the man and his horse, Finn told the Slothful Fellow that he could stay with his warriors for the night. "May the King of Lochlann live in fear of you for a dozen centuries, you brazen fellow. Go, my poor man, and gaze upon the noble beasts in that nearby meadow—there you will see what real horses are

Finn McCool and the Fianna

like. Take your wretched beast with you. Finn McCool allows you."

But Finn was hardly settled back to his chess match again, with Bald Conan opposite him, when he heard such a neighing and thunder of hooves from the pasture that he jumped to his feet and ran outside the tent to find the problem. There was the bony old horse, biting and kicking at the great war steeds of Finn McCool and his warriors, scattering them to all corners of the field.

"Dog of a sluggard, run to yon pasture and tie down your vicious beast! And don't let me see either of you ever again," yelled Finn at the top of his voice.

But the man shouted back, "Finn McCool, we will be at the other side of the mountain before your servants can reach the meadow. But let Conan come and seize it by the mane, and I'll guarantee that it shall be still." It was no sooner said than done, for Conan the Bald was swift of foot. Finn's warrior grabbed the horse's mane and it stood as if turned to stone.

"Get on him, Conan, and perhaps he'll move," suggested the man. So up leapt Conan, and strokes from his rod fell upon the horse's rump. Still it did not move, as if the bedraggled animal was rooted to the earth. "Ah, how could I forget? Put six of your best men on the horse. Then it will move," asserted the Slothful Fellow.

A half dozen of Finn's stoutest warriors now mounted the steed, along with the strange man who owned the horse. At his touch, the horse turned into a mighty stallion and raced off to the ocean faster than any arrow fired from the strongest bow. When they had reached the surging waves, the horse and all its riders galloped across the surf as if it were a meadow, then they disappeared into the sea foam. The last words of Finn McCool's warriors drifted back like the cry of lost gulls.

For the horse and man were druids of the Tuath de Danaan people, those who are ever-young and live beneath the sea. So Finn lost six of his bravest warriors in the flash of a second. And it was all because he would not believe.

Lanigan's Ball

In the town of Athy, one Jeremy Lanigan
    Battered away till he hadn't a pound,
His father he died and made him a man again,
    Left him a house and ten acres of ground!
He gave a grand party to friends and relations
    Who wouldn't forget him if he went to the wall;
And if you'll just listen, I'll make your eyes glisten
    With the rows and ructions of Lanigan's ball.

Myself, to be sure, got free invitations
For all the nice boys and girls I'd ask,
And in less than a minute the friends and relations
Were dancing as merry as bees round a cask.
Miss Kitty O'Hara, the nice little milliner,
Tipped me the wink for to give her a call,
And soon I arrived with Timothy Glenniher
Just in time for Lanigan's ball.

There was lashins of punch and wine for the ladies,
Potatoes and cakes and bacon and tay,
The Nolans, the Dolans, and all the O'Gradys
Were courting the girls and dancing away.
Songs they sung as plenty as water,
From "The Harp That Once Through Tara's Ould Hall,"
To "Sweet Nelly Gray" and the "Ratcatcher's Daughter,"
All singing together at Lanigan's ball.

They were starting all sorts of nonsensical dances,
Turning around in a nate whirligig;
But Julia and I soon scattered their fancies,
And tipped them the twist of a rale Irish jig.
Och mavrone! 't was then she got glad o' me;
We danced till we thought the old ceilin' would fall,
(For I spent a whole fortnight in Doolan's Academy
Learning a step for Lanigan's ball).

The boys were all merry, the girls were all hearty,
Dancin' around in couples and groups,

When an accident happened—young Terence McCarthy
He drove his right foot through Miss Halloran's hoops.
The creature she fainted and cried "Millia murther!"
She called for her friends and gathered them all;
Ned Carmody swore he'd not stir a step further,
But have satisfaction at Lanigan's ball.

In the midst of the row, Miss Kerrigan fainted—
And her cheeks all the while were as red as the rose—
And some of the ladies declared she was painted,
She took a small drop too much, I suppose.
Her lover, Ned Morgan, so powerful and able,
When he saw his dear Colleen stretched out by the wall,
He tore the left leg from under the table,
And smashed all the china at Lanigan's ball.

Oh, buys, but then was the ructions—
Myself got a lick from big Phelim McHugh,
But soon replied to his kind introductions,
And kicked up a terrible hullabaloo.
Old Casey the piper was near being strangled,
They squeezed his pipes, his bellows and all;
The girls in their ribbons they all got entangled,
And that put an end to Lanigan's ball.

by John Hand

Oisin in the Land of Youth

There once was a wicked king in the fairy kingdom of Tir na n-Og (the Land of Youth) who was the ruler for many years, holding court despite many opponents. The law said that every seven years the country's champions and warriors should stand for the king's crown.

So every seven years they all gathered in front of the palace and raced to the top of a hill about two miles afar. At the top of the mound was a chair. The first man to sit in that chair was crowned King of Tir na n-Og for the next seven years.

After he had ruled for lo these many generations, the current king was becoming weary and worried, fearing that someday someone would take his crown. So he asked his chief druid, "How long shall I keep the chair to rule this land? Will any man sit in it before me and take the crown from me?" The druid gathered his robes about him and responded, "You will keep the chair and the crown forever and ever. That is, unless your son-in-law snatches them both from you."

The king had no sons but he had a daughter, the most beautiful woman in Tir na n-Og. The likes of her could not be found anywhere in Ireland, nor in any kingdom in the world above or the world below. When the king heard the druid's warning, he proclaimed, "I will not have a son-in-law in this family! I'll just hide my daughter in such a way that no one will want to marry her."

Then he seized up a staff capable of casting spells, and he called his daughter before him. The king struck her with the staff and put a pig's head in place of her own. Then he sent the unfortunate girl away from his castle. Satisfied with his evil deed, the king turned to the druid and said, "Ah, no one will want her now, and my throne is mine forever."

The druid had seen what the king did to his daughter, and he was sad that he had given such information to the king. So, after some time, he went away to where the princess was being hidden.

"Must I always be this way?" she lamented. "Yes, you must be," he replied, "until you marry one of the sons of Finn McCool in Ireland. If you marry one of Finn's sons, you'll be well freed of this curse, and your head and beauty will return at once."

When the princess heard this, she was ready to leave Tir na n-Og immediately and come to Ireland so she could find a son of Finn McCool who would relieve her from her sad fate. She heard that Finn and his warriors and sons were living at the time on Knock an Ar, so she made her way to the place as fast as her chariot would take her. Hiding in the forest above their camp, she

Mountains of Valencia Island in County Kerry

spied on Oisin, one of Finn's most fair sons, and was pleased with his strength, good looks, and kindness.

It was usual for Finn and his men to go hunting in the mountains of Ireland. So on this day, Oisin, six warriors, and their great hounds had ventured out to find stags and hares for their dinner. They were so tired after killing all their wild game, they couldn't carry it all. So the men went back to camp to seek help and left Oisin alongside the kill, with Finn's magnificent dogs, to guard the cache.

The daughter of Tir na n-Og had followed the men on their hunt and watched the entire proceedings from a secret place. When she saw that Oisin was alone, she came down from her hiding place and presented herself to him. She offered to carry some of the game for him, so Oisin gave her a great bundle of the fresh meat and he carried the rest.

The day was very hot, and the load was heavy. So after many miles of walking, Oisin said, "Let us rest ourselves for a time until the heat passes." They both put down their loads and sat back against a great stone, lying in its shadow. The woman was quite warm, so she opened her dress a bit to cool off. Oisin looked over at her and was amazed and filled with wonder.

"It is a pity," he said, "that you have a pig's head on you, for I have never seen such a lovely woman in all my life."

She responded with her tale of woe, telling how her wicked father cast the spell of the pig's head upon her.

The princess went on to tell how the druid promised that if she married a son of Finn McCool, she would be freed from the magic. She also told him how she had watched him from afar and hoped that he would be the one to save her.

Oisin, ever the gentleman—and also thinking that this poor creature was certainly a lovely woman, if only she did not have a pig's head—responded, "If that is the problem, and if marriage with me will call an end to the spell, I'll agree. That pig's head will not be on you for long."

So they were married quickly, not waiting to take the game back to Finn McCool's camp. At the moment they declared their vows, the pig's head disappeared, and the most beautiful woman above and below the earth stood in front of Oisin.

"But unless you return with me to Tir na n-Óg we must part, because I cannot stay long in this world of humans."

"Never fear, my beloved. I will follow you wherever you need to go," said brave Oisin.

At once, they set out for Tir na n-Og, without so much as a by-your-leave to his father. They didn't stop on their journey until they came to the king's castle. That same year, there was to be another race to see who would be king. And all the great men of Tir na n-Og had gathered in front of the castle for the run up the hill to the chair. Oisin stood ready with the rest and reached the top of the hill before anyone else had even gained halfway. That was how the wicked king was finally deposed.

Now, Oisin and his lovely wife ruled Tir na n-Og for many happy years, and he was grateful. They were good and gracious rulers. But one day, he said that he would like to return to Ireland to see his father and his warriors.

His wife warned him, "If you return and set one foot on the earth of Ireland, you will never come back here to me, the Queen of Youth. You will become a blind old man. Do you know how long you have been here?"

Oisin said, "Three years?" He had no sense of time in the Land of Youth because time made no difference.

And she responded, "No, it has been more than three hundred years since you arrived in this kingdom after saving me. However, if you must return to Ireland to see your father, I will loan you this white steed to ride. But never set foot on the ground of Ireland, for you will be gone from me forever."

"Ah, my love, I will be back. Never fear," Oisin said, leaping into the saddle of silver and gold. "You are my reason to return. Yet I must have one more look at my father and my friends." Away he rode, faster than the wind, faster than the waves roaring upon the shores, faster than the eagle's flight.

Oisin never stopped the horse until he reached Ireland and rode on to Knock an Ar where he had last seen his father. There he saw a man tending a herd of cows in a field where there was a broad flat stone.

"Will you come here and flip over this stone?" Oisin asked the herdsman.

"Indeed, my lord, I cannot. I could not lift it, nor twenty times twenty warriors," he replied. So Oisin rode over to the stone and, reaching down, he caught it beneath his hand and turned it over. Underneath it was a great horn, the one Finn McCool used to rally his men.

"Please bring this horn to me," Oisin asked the frightened herdsman, who had never seen a man with such strength before. "I will not bring it to you," he said, "because I am not strong enough to lift it."

Oisin moved his horse closer to the horn and reached down to pick it up. But his foot slipped in the stirrups and touched the ground. In an instant, he was a blind old man and the warning of his lovely bride came true.

Beware of Dog

If you encounter a black dog with blazing red eyes, quickly make the sign of the cross. The dog will leap in the air and disappear, for it is merely the devil in disguise.

The Low-Backed Car

When I first met sweet Peggy,
'Twas on market day,
A low-backed car she drove, and sat
Upon a truss of hay.
But when that hay was blooming grass,
And decked with the flowers of spring,
No flower was there that could compare
With the blooming girl I sing.
As she sat in the low-backed car,
The man at the turnpike bar
Never did ask for the toll
But just rubbed his owld poll,
And looked after the low-backed car.

In battle's wild commotion,
The proud and mighty Mars
With hostile scythes demands his tithes
Of death—in warlike cars;
While Peggy, peaceful goddess,
Has darts in her right eye,
That knock men down in the market town,

As left and right they fly,—
While she sits in her low-backed car,
Than battle more dangerous far,
For the doctor's art
Cannot cure the heart
That is hit from that low-backed car.

Sweet Peggy round her car, sire,
Has strings of ducks and geese,
But the scores of hearts she slaughters
By far outnumber these,
While she among her poultry sits,
Just like a turtle dove,
Well worth the cage, I do engage,
Of the blooming god of love!
While she sits in her low-backed car
The lovers come from near and far,
And envy the chicken
That Peggy is pickin',
As she sits in the low-backed car.

O, I'd rather own that car, sir,
With Peggy by my side,
Than a coach and four, and gold galore,
And a lady for my bride.
For the lady would sit fornenst me
On a cushion made with taste,
While Peggy would sit beside me
With my arm around her waist,—

While we drove in the low-backed car
To be married by Father Mahar.
O, my heart would beat high
At her glance and her sigh,
Though it beat in a low-backed car!

by Samuel Lover

Niam

Mouth of the rose and hair like a cloud—
After my feet the wind grows loud:
The red East Wind whose rumor has gone
From Tir na n-Og* to Tir-na-Tonn.**
Under my feet the wildflower grows.
After my feet the shadows run,
Over my feet the long grass blows,
All things hail me and call me on,
Out of the darkness and into the sun,
Love and Beauty and Youth in one.

Under my feet the wildflower grows.
Men called me Niam when first arose

**Land of Youth ** Land Under the Sea*

My splendid star: but what now ye call
Me, do I heed if I hear at all?
Look in my eyes—are they gray or blue?
They are the eyes that the Fenians knew,
When out of the sunshine, into the shade,
I called to Oisin, and he obeyed.
Across Fionn's banner my dark hair flew,
And safe in its leash my love I drew.

I called to Oisin and he obeyed—
Out of the sunshine, into the shade,
Though the words were out and the warhorns blew
And wisdom and pride my voice gainsaid.
But a hundred years, or a thousand years,
I kept my lover from hopes and fears—
In Druid dark on my arm he slept.
Shall I not keep men even as I kept:
'Twixt a man and his wisdom let blow my hair,
The man is beside me, and wisdom's—where?

The Fenians died and the high Gods die
But spring's immortal, and so am I.
I am young, I am swift, I am fair to see,
My blood is the sap running new in the tree.
Shall I not keep men even as I kept
Oisin free from his falling sept?
Who shall deny me, or who gainsay,
For the world is beginning anew to-day?
Youth is glad, for the world is wide;

Tarry, O Youth! Love is here at thy side.
The world is beginning anew to-day;
Fire is awake in each clod of clay;
The ragweeds know what has never been told
By the old to the young, or the young to the old.
The hawthorns tell it in broad daylight;
The evening primrose awaits the night,
Her beautiful secret she shuts in close
Till the last late bee goes home from the rose.
And I am the secret, the flower, and the tree;
I am Beauty; O Youth, I have blossomed for thee.

by Mrs. W. H. Chesson (Nora Hopper)

The Rising of the Moon

Oh, then, tell me, Shawn O'Ferrall,
    Tell me why you hurry so?
Hush! *ma bouchal*, hush, and listen;
    And his cheeks were all a-glow:

The Rock of Cashel in Ireland

I bear orders from the Captain—
    Get you ready quick and soon;
For the pikes must be together
    At the risin' of the moon.

Oh, then, tell me, Shawn O'Ferrall,
    Where the gath'rin' is to be?
In the ould spot by the river,
    Right well known to you and me;
One word more—for signal token
    Whistle up the marchin' tune,
With your pike upon your shoulder
    By the risin' of the moon.

Out from many a mud-walled cabin
    Eyes were watchin' thro' that night;
Many a manly chest was throbbing
    For the blessed warning light.
Murmurs passed along the valleys,
    Like the banshee's lonely croon,
And a thousand blades were flashing
    At the risin' of the moon.

There, beside the singing river,
    That dark mass of men were seen—
Far above the shining weapons
    Hung their own beloved "Green";
Death to ev'ry foe and traitor!
    Forward! strike the marchin' tune,

And hurrah, my boys, for freedom!
    'T is the risin' of the moon.

Well they fought for poor Old Ireland
    And full bitter was their fate;
(Oh! what glorious pride and sorrow
    Fill the name of 'Ninety-Eight!)
Yet, thank God, e'en still are beating
    Hearts in manhood's burning non,
Who would follow in their footsteps
    At the risin' of the moon!

by John Keegan Casey

Ruins at Slea Head in County Kerry

The King of Ireland's Son

Now all away to Tir na n-Og are many roads that run,
But he has ta'en the longest lane, the King of Ireland's son.

Thee's roads of hate, and roads of love, and many a
middle way,
And castles keep the valleys deep where happy lovers
stray—

Where Aongus goes there's many a rose burns red mid
shadows dun,
Nor rose there is will draw his kiss, the King of Ireland's
son.

And yonder, where the sun is high, love laughs amid
the hay,
But smile and sigh have passed him by, and never make
delay.

And here (O! the sun is low) they're glad for harvest
won,

But naught he cares for wheat or tares, the King of
Ireland's son!

And you have flung love's apple by, and I'm to pluck it yet:
But what are fruits of gramarye with druid dews beset?

O what are magic fruits to him who meets the Lianan-
sidhe
Or hears athwart the distance dim Fionn's horn blow
drowsily!

He follows on forever when all your chase is done
He follows after shadows, the King of Ireland's son.

by Mrs. W. H. Chesson (Nora Hopper)

Ballymalis Castle in County Kerry

Chapter Two

Fairies, Spirits, and Things That Go Bump in the Night

He hammered and sang with tiny voice,
And sipped his mountain dew;
Oh! I laughed to think
he was caught at last,
But the fairy was laughing, too.

—*Robert Dwyer Joyce, "The Leprechaun"*

The Egg-Shell Brewery

Once in a town just south of the great city of Dublin, there was a young mother named Mary Sullivan. She had an infant son not more than one year old. Now her son was her darling and her pride, with his tousled yellow hair, bright blue eyes, and gentle, quiet disposition. At least, that's what Mary thought—and don't all mothers think the same of their darlings at first?

Well, one night things changed in the Sullivan household. For in the dark of black midnight, her healthy, fair-haired boy shriveled up to a wrinkled and cranky creature, who never stopped crying and squalling his head off.

But Mary's eyes were still clouded by a mother's love, and she did not see the change until the neighbors thought it best to get her alone for a talk.

"Sure, the child's not yours, Mary," her best friend said gently. "The fairies have taken your boy. It's a changeling you're nursing now."

Of course, this upset Mary a great deal, and she began to weep like the falls of the Shannon.

Another woman said, by way of comforting her, "Don't carry on so, Mary. The fairies have your boy to raise, and they've given you one of their own in exchange."

Somehow, this wasn't as comforting to Mary as it was meant to be. But gradually she grew attached to the changeling, even though its face was withered and its body was that of an old man shrunk to the size of a baby. Still, she said to herself, "It does look somewhat like my own darling boy."

So, despite the advice of friends, neighbors, and even the doctor, Mary didn't have the heart to toss the creature into the stove, or to burn off its nose with red hot tongs from the fireplace, or to throw it into the snow outside.

One day, a woman who went about the country by the name of Gray Helen, knocked at Mary's door. She was known to have many gifts, such as telling where the dead rested, how to charm away warts, and other such wonderful things of that nature...

"You're in grief, Mary Sullivan," were the first words she spoke when Mary opened the door.

"Aye, you may say that," said Mary. "And I have good cause to be so. My own fine child was taken from his cradle and an ugly piece of shriveled-up fairy child put in his place, without so much as a by-your-leave or beg-your-pardon."

"No blame to you, Mary," said Gray Helen. "But are you sure it's a fairy child you've got in your house?"

An Irish cottage

"Sure enough to no longer doubt my own eyes," sobbed Mary. "No mother's soul should know what I know!"

"Will you take this old woman's advice then, even though you may find it foolish?" asked Gray Helen.

"If it will bring me back my own darling, I'd throw sand in the fire or wear shoes as mittens or shave all my hair and wish that it'd never grow back," snapped Mary.

"Then do as I bid you," said Helen, "and you'll have your heart's desire. Put a kettle on the fire and make it boil like mad. Then get a dozen fresh-laid eggs, break them, throw away the insides, and put the shells into the boiling water. Offer the mixture to the babe, and you'll soon know if he's your own or a changeling."

So Mary did as she was told by Gray Helen. While she was toiling over the kettle, the child sat up in his cradle and watched her with a twinkle in his beady eyes. At last, his curiosity got the better of him, and he spoke with the voice of an old man.

"What are you about, Mammy?" he asked. The creature's use of speech betrayed his fairy blood.

Upon hearing that voice, Mary's heart rose to her throat and she almost choked. But she managed to contrive a smile and said, "I'm just at my brewing, darling."

"And what are you brewing there, Mammy?" asked the imp.

"Egg shells, my son," said Mary.

"Ahhh!" the changeling shrieked and clapped his hands together. "Fifteen hundred years I've been in the world, and I've never seen a brewery of egg-shells before. Give us a taste, Mammy! Give us a taste, quick about it."

So Mary took the ladle and carefully filled a sturdy mug, for the egg-shell brew was red-hot to the touch. When she offered it to the fairy, he grabbed it and threw it down his throat before you could say "Jack-jump-over-my-candlestick."

Then he gasped and gurgled and turned purple in the face and cried out, "I'm poisoned! Oh, Mammy, I'm poisoned."

Mary's anger was replaced by pity for the poor creature, and she took the ugly old thing and cradled it in her arms, singing the same soft lullaby she had sung for her own dear child. But soon enough the creature gasped his last breath and lay still in her arms.

Now, Mary didn't cry, but she didn't gloat either. In fact, she was mostly scared—scared to look at the dead fairy. When she was finally able to bring her eye to the little bundle, what should she see, but her own darling's sweet face and his soft round little arms and legs, all as still as a lake on a summer's day, save for the child's rosy mouth, which moved with his gentle breathing.

Now, who can describe the fountain of happiness that overflowed from Mary's heart at that moment? Not I, nor anyone who hasn't been a mother and cried both the tears of sorrow and the tears of happiness.

Rent Day Woes

"Oh, all is gone! All is gone!" muttered Bill Doody to himself as he sat on a rock by the Lake of Killarney. "This is a wide world, but what shall we do, and where shall we go? Tim the Driver swears if we don't pay our rent, he'll take every ha'penny we have.

To be sure, Judy and meself and the children will be turned out on the high road to starve. Ah, that I should have ever lived to see a day like this!"

Thus did hapless Bill Doody bemoan his fate to the reckless waves of the unfeeling lake, which seemed to mock his misery with its beauty. Yet Bill Doody was not so desolate as he supposed. For there was one listening to his sorrows, and help was at hand from an unexpected quarter.

"What's the matter, my good man?" asked a tall, portly gentleman who seemed to step out of nowhere. Bill was surprised to find the man standing in front of him, for he was seated on a rock that commanded the view of the whole plain. Bill asked himself if this gentleman might belong to another world, what with all the fairy islands that dotted the lake. He was worried, but mustered enough courage to reply.

"Oh, my crops have failed, someone has charmed away the butter from the churn, and now Tim the Driver will turn us out of our poor cottage if I don't pay every penny of the rent by noon tomorrow," Bill told the stranger.

"A sad story, indeed," said the gentleman, "but surely, if you just explained yourself to the agent, he wouldn't have the heart to turn you out."

"Heart!" exclaimed Bill. "Where would an agent get a heart?! I see you haven't had the honor of his company. Besides, Tim's had an eye on my farm for his own. I expect no mercy, and none will be received."

"Take this, poor fellow," said the gentlemen as he poured a purse full of gold coins into Bill's old hat, which lay on the ground. "Pay the man your rent, but leave it to me to see that it does him no good, for I remember a time when things went otherwise in this country. Why, then we would have hanged such a fellow in the twinkling of an eye."

But these words were lost on Bill, who saw only the gold and the fact that his farm was saved from Tim the Driver. When he regained his senses and lifted his head to thank the stranger, the man was gone.

"O'Donoghue, O'Donoghue!" shouted Bill to the lake. "The good, blessed O'Donoghue." For it was indeed the spirit of O'Donoghue, the great prince who lives under the waves of Killarney, who saved Bill. He ran home to Judy to show her the gold, and they rejoiced in their wealth and happiness.

The next day, Bill went to the agent's office, not with his hat in his hand, but bold and upright, like a man of independent means.

However, Tim the Driver did not greet him as an equal. "Take off your hat, Doody," he demanded. "Don't you know you're speaking to a magistrate?"

"I know I'm not speaking to the king," said Bill, "and I never takes off me hat but to them that I loves and respects. And I have neither for you or your kind."

"You scoundrel," raged Tim, biting his lips in anger at such unexpected opposition. "I'll teach you to be insolent. I have power in this county, you know."

A seaport in Connemara

"To the cost of the county," said Bill, whose head remained as firmly covered as the King of Kinsale himself.

"Well, where is your money?" asked the exasperated agent. "This is the rent day. If there's one penny missing, prepare to be turned out this very night."

"There is your rent," said Bill, laying the gold coins on the table. "You'd better count it out and give me a receipt that says I paid in full."

Tim the Driver looked with amazement on the gold. It was the real thing, not some dirty old notes that are only fit to light your pipe with, but solid gold coins. However much Tim wanted to ruin Bill Doody and take his farm, he loved gold still better. So he took the coins and stacked them while he counted. When he was finished, he handed a receipt marked "paid in full" to Bill.

As Tim the Driver stared from his door, Bill strutted down the high street like a cat with clean whiskers. But as Tim turned back to his table, he found not the gold coins, but a stack of old gingerbread cakes, each stamped like a guinea with the king's head.

Tim raged and he cursed, but to no avail. For the gold had become gingerbread, and Bill had the receipt in his pocket. So he saw there was no use in saying a thing about the affair, for he would only become the laughing-stock of the whole town.

From that hour, all of Bill Doody's undertakings prospered, and he became rich. He continued to visit the rock by the shore of the Lake of Killarney and bless the day he met with the great O'Donoghue.

The Fairy Nurse

Sweet babe! a golden cradle holds thee,
And soft the snow-white fleece enfolds thee;
In airy bower I'll watch thy sleeping,
Where branchy trees to the breeze are sweeping.
    Shuheen, sho, lulo lo!
When mothers languish broken-hearted,
When young wives are from husbands parted,
Ah! little think the keeners lonely,
They weep some time-worn fairy only.
    Shuheen, sho, lulo lo!
Within our magic halls of brightness,
Trips many a foot of snowy whiteness;
Stolen maidens, queens of fairy—
And kings and chiefs a sluagh-shee airy.
    Shuheen, sho, lulo lo!
Rest thee, babe! for soon thy slumbers
Shall flee at the magic koelshie's* numbers;
In airy bower I'll watch thy sleeping,
Where branchy trees to the breeze are sweeping.
    Shuheen, sho, lulo lo!

by Edward Walsh

* *ceol-sidhe—fairy music*

The Fairy Gold

Buttercups and daisies in the meadow,
And the children pick them as they pass,
Weaving in the sunlight and the shadow,
Garlands for each little lad and lass;
Weave with dreams their buttercups and daisies,
As the poor dead children did of old.
Will the dreams, like sunshine in their faces,
Wither with their flowers like Fairy Gold?

Once, when lonely in Life's crowded highway,
Came a maiden sweet, and took my hand,
Led me down Love's green delightful byway,
Led me dreaming back to Fairyland.
But Death's jealous eye that lights on lovers
Looked upon her, and her breast grew cold,
And my heart's delight the green sod covers,
Vanished from my arms like Fairy Gold!

Then to Ireland, my long-suffering nation,
That poor hope life left me yet I gave:
With her dreams I dreamed, her desolation
Found me, called me, desolate by that grave.
Once again she raised her head, contending

For her children's birthright as of old;
Once again the old fight had the old ending,
All her hopes and dreams were Fairy Gold.

Now my work is done and I am dying,
Lone, an exile on a foreign shore;
But in dreams I roam with my heart's lying,
Lonely in the old land I'll see no more.
Buttercups and daisies in the meadows
When I'm gone will bloom; new hopes for old.
Comfort her with sunshine after shadows,
Fade no more away like Fairy Gold.

by John Todhunter

A meadow of flowers in County Kerry

The Fairies

Brave old Ireland is the land of fairies, but of all the various descriptions, there isn't one to be compared with the leprechaun, in the regard of cunning and cuteness. Now if you don't know what a leprechaun is, I'll tell you. Why, then—save us and keep us from harm, for they are queer chaps to *gosther* about—a leprechaun is the fairies' shoemaker: and a mighty conceited little fellow he is, I assure you, and very mischievous.

by John Brogham

Fairy Music

Irish dance and music are celebrated throughout the world. It is said that their inspiration comes from the fairies. This story is told in County Clare:

A young man named Colin returned to his cottage after a long day of cutting peat. There, he found a lovely young woman sitting by his fire. She was softly humming a sad tune to herself. Colin had never seen the beautiful woman before, but he immediately fell in love with her.

He asked, "Ah, what is that lovely, sad song you're singing?"

The young woman looked at him blankly, as if she had just noticed he was there. "I've lost it," she said.

"Lost what?" Colin asked.

"I've been with the fairies," she replied. "I was fetching water, when I slipped and fell. When I got up, it was like the hills glowed. Then I heard it, the fairy

"The Fairy Dance" (early 20th-century illustration)

music. It was soft and pretty and low and beautiful. Then I forgot why I'd come to the well, and I forgot my da and ma and the little ones waiting for me.

"The music charmed me, you see. Soon, there were fairies all around me. Beautiful people they were, dressed in silver and gold. They were dancing to the sweetest music. And then a young man took my hand, and we danced 'til the moon and the stars left the sky. It was like floating on the air.

"The young man was a fairy prince, and they had charmed me to be his bride. To think of it! Me—a fairy princess. But then a man with flaming red hair thrust a branch of ivy into my hands. He said only one word, 'Remember,' and then all my life came rushing back to me—my parents and brothers and sisters and our little cottage—and I got scared. I started to run. I could hear the fairies coming, so I ran harder and harder. I've been running the whole night."

Colin said, "But you've got away. There are no fairies here to scare you anymore. You won't be lost for long."

The young woman looked up at Colin with tears in her eyes. "No, you don't understand. It's the fairy music I've lost. There's a memory of it in my head, but I can't find it anymore. If I don't hear it again, I'll die."

So Colin took her into his life and married her, and he called her Kathleen, because she liked the way it sounded. He spent the rest of his life trying to please her, making up songs, learning to play the harp and the whistle and the pipes. And they lived a happy life together. But every full moon, Kathleen stepped outside and again sang her unknown song to herself, trying to find the words and melody to the lost fairy music.

John Hanifin and the Fairies

Not far from this very place lived a man by the name of John Hanifin. He was a great farmer, with wide fields and many cattle. The cows were driven from the barn every morning up to the milking ground, which was a large grassy pasture in front of Hanifin's home. In the center of the space was placed a large tub. Each milkmaid poured her pail of milk into the tub as soon as she finished filling it.

One sunshiny morning, the tub was turned over and all the milk poured out upon the ground. The same thing occurred the next morning, and the next. John Hanifin grew worried because no matter how closely the maids watched, or how much more careful they became, the milk always spilled.

Dairy cattle grazing in Cork

Naturally, Hanifin's wife was very angry about this, and she constantly scolded the maids. They grew very afraid of her and tried hard to keep an eye on the tub. But the milk continued to be spilled for more than a week.

Hanifin grew tired of this and decided to drive his herd to another location. On his way, he passed an old fairy fort on the road between his house and the new pasture. As the cattle walked past, he heard a child crying. The babe was answered by a woman's voice that said, "Hush-ye now, my little one. Hanifin's cows are passing, and soon we'll have milk enough."

Hanifin listened with wide eyes, but he was wise enough not to say anything. So while the next milking was going on, he kept a close watch on the tub. He never let his eyes off the milk. As one of the maids was finished milking, she walked toward the tub but was knocked into it by a heifer who was pushed by another cow. Naturally, everything spilled. Out came the wife, screaming and yelling about the loss of the milk again.

Hanifin stopped her yelling by saying, "This is no fault of the maids. They can't help it, so I'll manage this." He was quiet as he planned what to do.

The next morning, he went about his chores as usual. And again he heard the child crying inside the fairy fort. As he walked by, he bravely said out loud, "Tomorrow, a cow of mine will calve. No one will milk that cow; you can do what you like with the milk." And he walked on with the herd.

The tub was not turned over the next morning nor ever again. But Hanifin's wife did not know what had happened. She tried to milk the cow with the newborn calf, but she always found that someone had gotten there before her. Naturally, she grew angry, thinking that someone was stealing the milk. Hanifin told her not to worry, because he knew what was happening.

This went on for two years. Hanifin prospered and his cows continued to give rich, foaming milk every day... all but from the one cow that he had set aside.

Hanifin was a very generous man, and he always helped his neighbors when they got into trouble. He often aided them in paying their debts. Yet at last when the creditors demanded all their money, they came after Hanifin because he had secured the loans of his desperate friends. The creditors intended to take everything from Hanifin, from his house to his cows.

The bailiff arrived early one day, planning to take what he could carry and drive off the herd for sale. Hanifin ran to the fairy fort and said, "I'm going to lose all my cows, but I'll try to save the one I kept for you and feed her still so the child may have its daily milk."

The bailiff sent down three of his men to round up the cattle. They went to the pasture where the cows were grazing and began to drive them down the road. As each deputy passed the fairy fort, he was picked up by some unseen hand and tossed over the hedgerow into a bog. One minute he was on this side of the road, and the next minute he was in the ditch. The deputies were so battered and bruised with all this, they became extremely frightened and complained that people were beating them up. They did not know who it was, but they blamed Hanifin. The cattle, of course, lifted their tails and galloped back to their pasture.

The next day, the bailiff sent out a posse of armed men to take Hanifin's cattle and tear down his house. But as they were driving the herd away, they had to pass the fairy fort. Before they could bless themselves, they were tossed from the road, over the hedgerows, and into the muddy bog. They were cut and wounded from the thorns and thistles as they tried to crawl out.

The cows ran back to their pasture, since the officers could barely move. Never again did the bailiff send his deputies to take away Hanifin's cows, and the creditors never did collect their money. Hanifin prospered from selling all the milk, and he continued to help his neighbors. Eventually, all the debts were paid off, and everyone was pleased.

Beware the Banshee

The banshee are a peculiarly Irish sort of ghost. Originally, they were beautiful young maidens who carried away potential suitors to Tir na n-Og, the land of perpetual youth. Eventually, the pretty girls evolved into the screeching, withered hags with wild eyes and flaming hair known as the banshee.

The banshee appear to those whose death is imminent. They beckon the doomed into that unknown spirit world with a shriek of terror that sounds like the long drawn-out wailing of a tormented soul. It is said that the banshee haunt only those who can trace their roots to the ancient royal Irish families. One can only wish to be spared this inheritance.

The Piper and the Pooka

In long-ago days, there was a fool (but only half a fool) living in Dunmore in far-off County Galway. Although he was truly fond of the pipes, he could not learn more than one tune, "The Black Rogue." But he got a lot of money from the fine gentlemen of the county, because they teased him for sport after he played.

One night, the piper was wandering home from a party where there'd been plenty o' drink and dancing. When he came across a little bridge that was near his mother's house, he squeezed the pipes and began playing "The Black Rogue." From the midnight darkness, a Pooka—that wicked fairy beast—came up from behind the poor piper and flung the man on his broad, hairy back. There were long, sharp horns on the Pooka, and the piper got a fine grip on them.

"Destruction to you, you vile creature. Let me fly home. I have a ten-penny coin in my pocket for my wonderful mother, and she wants a pinch o' snuff," the man cried out.

"Never mind your fine mother," retorted the evil Pooka. "But keep your grip. If you fall, you will shatter your back and your pipes." And the Pooka told him to play another tune, "The Shan Van Vocht."

"Mitheree!" wailed the piper. "I don't know it!"

"Never mind whether you know it or not," warned the beast. "Play up, and I'll make your fingers fast and the tune elegant."

The worried piper put wind in his bag, and then he played such magnificent music, he himself wondered where it came from.

"My word, you're but a fine bit of music teacher," said the piper. "But now, tell me where we're going."

"Now just you listen, my questioning lad," said the Pooka, delighted with the music the piper could now play. "There's a grand feast in the great house upon the hill, the home of the Banshee, atop Croagh Patrick tonight. That's where we'll flee," he explained in his low, rumbling voice. "I'm bringing you there to play your music, and you'll be paid handsomely, believe me."

"Upon my word," rejoined the piper. "You will save me a pilgrimage then. For Father William in the church down below put a journey of penance for me to the top of Croagh Patrick because I stole a white gander from him last Martinmas."

Then the Pooka flew with the frightened piper across hills high and low, and over bogs low and murky. They came to the top of Croagh Patrick all in a rush of rolling thunder and flashing lighting, much to the fear of the piper. Atop the mountain, the Pooka struck the rocks with three sharp blows of his cloven hoof. A magnificent oak door swung open, and the Pooka and the piper passed below together. The door slammed shut behind them.

Ah, it was a fine sight that greeted the piper. The grand room was decorated with furs, linens, and jewels. The piper saw a golden table in the center of the hall that was surrounded by hundreds of old hags sitting on stumps of logs. They looked up, and the oldest of the old screeched out, "Who is this ye have with ye, oh fine Pooka of November? Who is this?"

The Pooka responded, "None other than the best piper in Ireland!"

At this, the poor piper turned white as the salt sea foam, but he continued to clutch his pipes, for he was truly afraid.

One of the ancient ones hit the ground with her blackthorn walking stick, and a wide door opened in the side of the hall. What did the piper see, but the white gander he had stolen from Father William.

"Well, by my true conscience then, myself and my mother ate every bit o' that fine gander! Only one wing did I save, which I gave to Red Mary in the next valley. It was she that told the priest I stole the gander."

The gander did not pay any attention to the piper's tale because it was busy a-clearing the table of all the mugs and plates. Then, the Pooka told the piper to play. At this, the old women leapt up and began dancing. They danced and danced until they collapsed with exhaustion.

As the last of the piper's notes died away, the Pooka told them to pay the man. Each of the hags drew out a gold coin from their wolf-skin purses, and they gave the coins to the piper.

"Now come with me," said the Pooka. "It is time to go home."

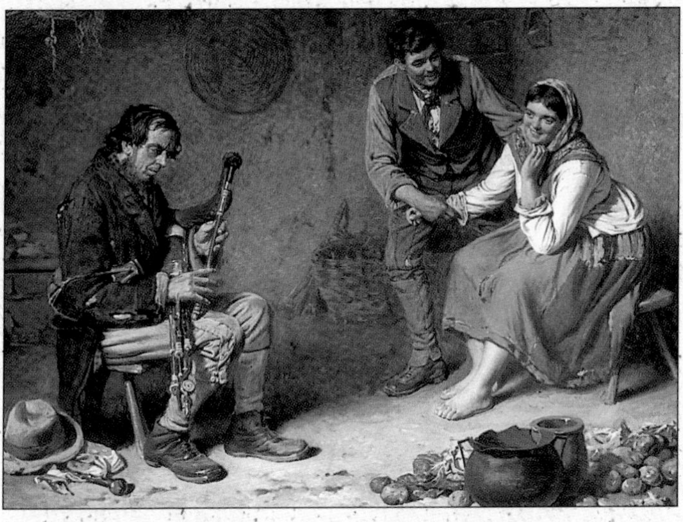

"The Overture" by Edwin Thomas Roberts

Out they went then. Just as the piper was about to jump on the Pooka's back, the gander came up to him and presented him with a wonderful set of new pipes. It was not long before the Pooka had carried the piper back to Dunmore. Off jumped the piper at the little bridge.

Before he left in the night, the Pooka said, "You have two things now you didn't have before: You have sense, and you have music. Now go."

The piper scurried home and banged on his mother's door. "Let me in, let me in! I'm as rich as the earl, and I'm the best piper in Ireland."

"You're drunk," said his mother, always the doubter for she knew her son.

"No, for sure! No, indeed," the man rejoined. "I haven't had a drop."

Irish countryside along the Atlantic coast

The mother then let him in, and she was truly amazed when he handed her all the gold coins and showed off his new pipes. "Wait now," he said. "Wait until you hear the music I'll sound."

He buckled on the pipes. But instead of glorious music, there was only the sound of geese and ganders honking and calling, as if all the birds in Ireland were screeching. All the neighbors rose from their sleep and came to his mother's house, where they stood outside and mocked him.

But they quieted down when he put on his old pipes and played the most wonderful tunes, the best they had ever heard.

The next dawn, when his mother arose from bed and went to the hiding place where she had placed the coins, all she found were dried leaves.

At this the piper went to Father Martin and told him his story of the Pooka, the old women, and the gander. The priest, of course, did not believe a word of this until the piper played him a tune on the new pipes. Again, came the honking and screeching of geese. "Get away, get away, you thief!" roared the priest.

But the piper put down his new pipes and put on his old, just to show the priest that everything he had said was true.

From then on, the piper played only the most wonderful music that County Galway had ever heard. He became quite wealthy playing far and near. And there was never another piper quite as good as he.

The Fairy Fiddler

'T is I go fiddling, fiddling,
By weedy ways forlorn:
I make the blackbird's music
Ere in his breast 't is born;
The sleeping larks I waken
'Twixt the midnight and the morn.

No man alive has seen me,
But women hear me play
Sometimes at door or window,
Fiddling the souls away—
The child's soul and the colleen's—
Out of the covering clay.

None of my fairy kinsmen
Make music with me now:
Alone the raths I wander,
Or ride the whitethorn bough;
But the wild swans they know me,
And the horse that draws the plow.

by Mrs. W. H. Chesson (Nora Hopper)

The Leprechaun's Revenge

Leprechauns are Ireland's best-known fairies. They are often depicted as merry, industrious little sprites with green hats and a shillelagh. In fact, they are the tinkers of the fairy race, in charge of the tailoring and shoemaking chores for the fairy gentry. Their name means "Artisan of the Brogue."

They know all about hidden treasure and, if it takes their fancy, they will sometimes guide a person of goodwill to the very spot in a fairy ring where a pot of gold lies buried. But leprechauns can be mischievous if they become offended and, as they become offended easily, one should be cautious and civil in dealing with them, as a County Kerry farmer named Tim found out.

Now one day Tim was in the fields hoeing his potatoes, when he spied a little fellow, not bigger than the back of Tim's hand, mending a tiny pair of shoes under the shade of a weed's leaf. Tim recognized him as a leprechaun and, like a cat stalking a mouse, he silently made his way to the little fellow's workplace. When he got close enough, he grabbed for the creature, caught him by his coat, and lifted him into his pocket.

Tim ran home as fast as he could. He bolted through the door to his cottage and drew the curtain across the window. Taking the chain from his pocket watch, he fastened it about the leprechaun's neck. As soon as he was satisfied that the fairy was secure, Tim spoke.

"Now, tell me," he said, "where's your pot of gold? Tell me quickly or I'll bind you tighter."

"I do not know of any pot of gold," said the leprechaun, irritated at being treated so roughly. "Now, let me go so I may finish mending the king's shoes."

"If that's your game," Tim said, "then we'll see how you like this." With those words, Tim laid the leprechaun on the smoldering coals in the grate and scorched him.

"Oh, take me off, take me off!" cried the leprechaun. "I'll tell you what you need to know."

But Tim kept the little fellow suspended over the hot coals until he revealed his secret. "All right, all right," the leprechaun said. "Look in the bottom of the old quarry, under the stones by the garden wall, and you'll find your pot of gold. Only you must go at midnight—and beware the man who takes his wife along."

Now it just so happened that at this very moment, Tim's wife came in with a pail of fresh milk. Seeing the leprechaun suspended above the fire caused her to lose her wits for just a moment. In that moment, the pail dropped, and the milk spilled all over the floor.

Tim's wife was very angry and began to hit the leprechaun with her broom saying, "Go away, you little wretch! You have cursed the milk and brought ill luck to this house. Go away!" And she kicked the leprechaun out of the house.

Tim told his wife what the leprechaun had said about the pot of gold, and they agreed he should go that very night. She agreed to stay home and not stir about. But as midnight approached, she thought to herself, *Why, if I should get to the quarry before Tim, I would have the gold to myself, for sure enough if he gets it, I will have nothing.*

Before she even finished her thought, her feet were racing to the quarry. When she arrived, no trace of Tim could be found. It was so dark that she lost her way, and she tripped and fell to the bottom of the quarry. There she lay groaning, for her leg was broken.

When Tim arrived, he was already frightened by the dark night and the fairies' magic. Then he came to the edge of the quarry and heard groans coming from below.

"Mary's breath upon us!" he shouted. "What is that down there? Are you evil or are you good?"

"Oh, it's your own wife here, and my leg is broken," cried the woman. "Come down and help me or I'll die if you don't, and my curses will be on you forever."

So Tim slowly made his way down to his wife, muttering to himself all the time, "Is this my pot of gold at the bottom of the quarry?"

Tim took his wife home and she recovered, but she walks with a limp to this day, from the curse of the leprechaun upon her. Tim's neighbors say that his wife is the leprechaun's curse on him. As to the pot of gold, no one has ever found it. And the little leprechaun still sits under the shade of the weed's leaf and laughs as he tinkers away at his shoes with a tiny hammer. But all are afraid to touch him, for they know how he can take his revenge.

To the Leanán Sidhe*

Where is thy lovely perilous abode?
    In what strange phantom-land
Glimmer the fairy turrets whereto rode
    The ill-starred poet band?

Say, in the Isle of Youth hast thou thy home,
    The sweetest singer there,
Stealing on winged steed across the foam
    Through the moonlit air?

* *To the Fairy Bride*

Or, where the mists of bluebell float beneath
    The red stems of the pine,
And sunbeams strike thro' shadow, dost thou breathe
    The word that makes him thine?

Or by the gloomy peaks of Erigal,
    Haunted by storm and cloud,
Wing past, and to thy lover there let fall
    His singing-robe and shroud?

Or is thy palace entered thro' some cliff
    When radiant tides are full,
And round thy lover's wandering, starlit skiff,
    Coil in luxurious lull?

And would he, entering on brimming flood,
    See caverns vast in height.
And diamond columns, crowned with leaf and bud,
    Glow in long lanes of light,

And there, the pearl of that great glittering shell
    Trembling, behold thee lone,
Now weaving in slow dance an awful spell,
    Now still upon thy throne?

Thy beauty! ah, the eyes that pierce him thro'
    Then melt as in a dream;
The voice that sings the mysteries of the blue
    And all that Be and Seem!

Thy lovely motions answering to the rhyme
 That ancient Nature sings,
That keeps the stars in cadence for all time,
 And echoes thro' all things!

Whether he sees thee thus, or in his dreams,
 Thy light makes all lights dim;
An aching solitude from henceforth seems
 The world of men to him.

Thy luring song, above the sensuous roar,
 He follows with delight,
Shutting behind him Life's last gloomy door,
 And fares into the Night.

by Thomas Boyd

Larry the Piper

In the county of Tipperary, you'll find one of the strangest-shaped hills in all of Ireland. Its peak is like a nightcap that has been carelessly tossed on your head, and landed sticking straight up to Heaven. At its very point is a fairy ring, or rath, as the fairies call them. These raths are very sacred ground to fairies, for it is in these places that they hold all their midnight revels.

The fairies become very angry when a farmer shows disrespect to them by allowing his bulls and cows to graze all over their raths. It's not just the trampling of their rude hooves that upsets the fairies, but also the sound of their lowing—it's so sad in fairy ears, it causes them to cry.

Now, it happened that the farmer who owned this hill did not believe in fairies, and he wasn't about to waste valuable grazing space on some superstitious nonsense. In fact, he made it a point to tell his herdsmen to let the cows graze wherever they wanted.

The sounds of the cows mooing and the bulls bellowing made the fairies very sad, so the Queen of the Fairies determined to drive the cattle away by whatever means necessary.

At first, she tried to scare the poor animals themselves. She changed herself into a fly and bit the creatures until they scampered about as if mad. The cattle's troubles would last until the sun rose over the hill, so that the cows were so tired from want of rest, they wouldn't give any milk. And never a night passed that some wouldn't fall into a pit or tumble into a river.

But the farmer was determined to use all his land, so he hired more herdsmen to tend the cattle at night. Thus, the Fairy Queen was forced to turn her attentions to the men out on the hillsides.

Cattle grazing in Connemara

At midnight every night, she appeared in a different form. One time, she was a great horse with wings like an eagle, diving and shrieking at the herdsmen. Another night, she turned into a little man with a bull's head and a tongue of flame who roared about the hillsides.

The poor herdsmen would cover their faces and call on the saints for help, but it did them no good. With a puff of her breath, the queen blew away the folds of their coats and caused them to gaze upon the terrors, their teeth ready to fall out from the chattering.

Soon, all the herdsman quit, and the farmer could find no one to tend his cattle. It looked as if the fairies had beaten him, with his substance dwindling daily and the rent day coming 'round.

Now at that time in Tipperary, there lived a man named Larry Hoolahan, who played the pipes better than any other man in the country. Larry was known as a dashing blade who feared nothing. It was said that with enough whiskey, he would defy the devil himself.

So, as his last hope, the farmer sent for Larry and told him of his troubles.

"If that is all that ails you, rest easy," said Larry. "Were there as many fairies in Tipperary as there are potato blossoms, I would face them down. It would be a queer thing, indeed, if I, who am not afraid of a proper man, should turn my back upon a brat of sprite not bigger than my thumb."

"Don't talk so bold," said the anxious farmer, who now believed in the fairies' magic. "You do not know who might hear you. But if you can stay with my herd for one week on the top of the hill, than you shall have a free hand with all I have until the sun itself burns to ash."

With the bargain struck, Larry went that night to the hilltop. He carried with him a bottle of barleycorn and his pipes to keep him company. He sat on a big rock in the middle of the rath and began a pleasant tune on the pipes. Almost at once, he heard the laughing voices of the fairies upon the rath.

"What? Another man upon our sacred ring?" they cried. "Go to him, Queen, and make him repent his rashness."

Then Larry saw a small black cat sitting on one of the outer stones of the ring. Presently, the cat swelled up toward the sky and took the shape of a towering bull. But before it could begin to roar, Larry took out his pipes and said, "Very good. If you'll lead the dance, I'll pipe."

He struck up a merry reel. The queen turned from bull to dragon to horse to fish, but still Larry played on. The queen lost patience with this game, as ladies do when you don't mind their scolding. She changed herself into a calf, as white as the cream of Cork and with eyes as mild as those of a lovely, young girl.

The calf came up to Larry, fawning and gentle, to throw him off his guard. But Larry was not so easily deceived. For when she came up, he dropped his pipes and leapt upon her back.

Now the queen rejoiced, for she thought she had the young man in her power. With one great spring, she jumped clear from the mountain right across the broad waters of the Shannon, flowing more than ten miles away.

This was all accomplished in less than a second, and when she lighted on the opposite bank of the river, she kicked up her heels, flinging Larry to the ground.

Larry looked the calf straight in the face and said, "By my word, well done! That was not a bad leap for a calf."

The Fairy Queen looked Larry straight in the face and suddenly assumed her natural shape. "Lawrence," she said, "you are a bold fellow. Will you come back the way you went?"

"That I will, if you'll let me," said Larry.

The queen changed back to the calf, and with another bound they found themselves again at the fairy rath on top of the mountain. Resuming her natural self, the queen addressed Larry. "You have shown so much courage, Lawrence, that while you keep herds on this hill, you shall never be bothered by me or mine. If you need my services for anything else, all you need do is play on your pipes."

With this she vanished. And never did she reappear to trouble Larry, and he did not trouble her with his requests. For he ate and drank at the farmer's expense and roosted in the fairy rath, only occasionally casting an eye to the flock, because he knew they were safe from harm.

A Little Woman in Red

'Twas about six o'clock on a crisp autumn morning not so long ago. The harvesters were in the fields early, although the dew was still upon the oats. The grass was lush on the soft, green hills, perfect for the cattle heading out from the milking barns. Tommy Owen was at the edge of the field with his reaping hook, standing on the shore road between Carraroe and Galway.

He was looking over the field of grain swaying gently in the breeze, when he felt a presence beside him. Looking down, he saw a shoeless little woman wearing a red petticoat and a shawl around her head. "God bliss your work," she said to him. "Ah, sure to you, too," replied Tommy—admitting later that he was a bit startled.

"Can ye show me the road to Galway?" asked the little woman in red.

"Look there," said Tommy, pointing to the main highway far beyond the field.

"But could I not get to the road this way?" she inquired, waving her hand over the peat bog to the right.

"Well, ye could," your man said. "But it wouldn't be aisy. If you go over there across the field, you'll have nothin' to do but get on the road. And ye'll only have that little wall to cross."

"I'll go the way I think is best meself," said she and disappeared quicker than Tommy could make the sign of the cross. He was terribly frightened because he knew that the little lady in red was certainly not of this earth.

by Daniel Deeney

The Dingle Peninsula in Ireland

The Leprechaun, or Fairy Shoemaker

Little cowboy, what have you heard,
    Up on the lonely rath's green mound?
Only the plaintive yellow bird
    Singing in sultry fields around?
Chary, chary, chary, chee-e!
Only the grasshopper and the bee?
    "Tip-tap, rip-rap,
    Tick-a-tack-too!
    Scarlet leather sewn together,
    This will make a shoe.
    Left, right, pull it tight,
    Summer days are warm;
    Underground in winter,
    Laughing at the storm!"
Lay your ear close to the hill:
    Do you not catch the tiny clamor,
    Busy click of an elfin hammer,
Voice of the Leprechaun singing shrill
    As he merrily plies his trade?

He's a span
And a quarter in height:
Get him in sight, hold him fast,
And you're a made Man!

You watch your cattle the summer day,
Sup on potatoes, sleep in the hay;
How should you like to roll in your carriage
And look for a duchess' daughter in marriage?
Seize the shoemaker, so you may!
"Big boots a-hunting,
Sandals in the hall,
White for a wedding feast,
And pink for a ball:
This way, that way,
So we make a shoe,
Getting rich every stitch,
Tick-tack-too!"
Nine-and-ninety treasure crocks,
This keen miser-fairy hath,
Hid in mountain, wood, and rocks
Ruin and round-tower, cave and rath,
And where the cormorants build;
Four times of old
Guarded by him;
Each of them filled
Full to the brim
With gold.

I caught him at work one day myself,
    In the castle-ditch where the foxglove grows;
A wrinkled, wizened, and bearded elf,
    Spectacles stuck on the top of his nose,
    Silver buckles to his hose,
    Leather apron, shoe in his lap;
    "Rip-rap, tip-tap,
    Tick-tack-too!
    A grig stepped on my cap,
    Away the moth flew.
    Buskins for a fairy prince
    Brogues for his son,
    Pay me well, pay me well,
    When the job's done."
The rogue was mine beyond a doubt,
    I stared at him; he stared at me!
    "Servant, sir!" "Humph!" said he,
    And pulled a snuff box out.
He took a long pinch, looked better pleased,
    The queer little Leprechaun;
    Offered the box with a whimsical grace,—
Pouf! he flung the dust in my face,—
    And, while I sneezed,
    Was gone!

by William Allingham

Coomakesta Pass, Ballinskelligs Bay, Ring of Kerry

Chapter Three

This Mythical Landscape

Hills as green as emeralds
Cover the countryside
Lakes as blue as sapphires—
Are Ireland's special pride
And rivers that shine like silver
Make Ireland look so fair—
But the friendliness of her people
Is the richest treasure there.

—Irish Blessing

The Creation of Lake Killarney

A knight from a distant land decided to woo the fair daughter of a rich Kerry farmer in the Killarney valley. Now, the knight was not well versed in the ways of love. Instead of following the courting rituals and proposing marriage as he ought, he urged the girl to depart immediately with him to his castle in the north.

While the girl was earnestly in love with the knight—and took no pains to conceal her love—she made it known that she would never leave her native vale unless it was as the knight's lawfully married wife.

The knight struggled between his pride and his love for the maiden, but he finally went to the girl's house to request her hand from her parents. The parents, who found the match to be a good one, agreed at once, and so the knight went out to seek his bride. Her maid told him that, as was the custom when a girl was in love, she had gone to the fairy well in the valley for water and to seek her fortune.

The knight ran to the well and found his bride with two of her handmaids at the spring's edge. The handmaids were just leaving the well with their full buckets balanced on their heads. But the girl's pitcher was only half filled, and she was just about to dip it into the well again when she saw her lover.

Before the girl could express her surprise and displeasure that he was still pursuing her, the knight told her where he had been and what he had said to her parents. In a moment, the lass could think of nothing but her newfound happiness.

Her pitcher was set aside, and in the cool evening air, the knight and his bride walked about the rocks and bushes of the valley, talking and dreaming of their future life together. The half-filled pitcher was forgotten, and the time went by without notice.

Suddenly, as the happy couple approached her father's house, the maid remembered the pitcher and the fateful nature of the magical spring. She shrieked and rushed headlong down the side of the valley back toward the well. Her knight followed quickly and soon caught her up in his strong arms.

"What does this mean?" he asked with desperation. "Do you not want me for your husband?"

"No, no," said the girl with equal fervor, "you don't understand. It's the well and the pitcher I left behind. If I don't get to it and fill it full, then. . . ."

But it was already too late. For in front of them, a sheet of water was already covering the little hill where the well stood. And from the well itself, a fountain of water was bursting forth. The water was lapping at the couple's feet when the knight leapt into action.

The Lake of Killarney in County Kerry

The girl stood there like a statue and would have been covered and drowned were it not for the strength of the knight. Lifting her on his shoulders, he slogged his way through the swiftly rising waters to the nearest slope. Then he made his way to the girl's home just in time to give warning to all the valley's inhabitants to gain the heights before their dwellings were covered with water.

The young maid's neglect was denounced by all, but neither she nor the knight cared because, lawfully married or not, they had soon departed for his own country. But their careless love has left Ireland with the most beautiful lake in the world: Killarney.

An Elegy

This was an ancient poem, sung in Gaelic and accompanied by a harp, written about the Boyne River by an Ard-Fhile, the chief poet of the High King:

O Boyne, once famed for battles, sports, and conflicts,
And great heroes of the race of Conn,
Art thou grey after all thy blooms?

O aged old woman of grey-green pools,
O wretched Boyne of many tears.

Where is the glory of thy sires?
The glory of Art with the swift arrow;
Of Meíltan, with the swift-darting spears;
Of the lordly race of the O'Neil?
To thee belonged red victory,
When the Fenian wrath was kindled,
And the heroes in thousands rode to war,
And the bridles clanked on the steeds.

O river of kings and the sons of kings,
Of the swift bark and the silver fish,
I lay my blessing on thee with my tears,
For thou art the watcher by a grave—
My treasures lie in the earth at thy side—
O Boyne of many tears.

My sons lie there in their strength,
My little daughter in her beauty—
Rory, and Brian, and Rose—
These I have given against my will,
My blood, my heart, my bone and kin,
My love and my life, to the grave.

The blessing of men was on them,
The blessings of thousands that loved them,
From Kells of the Crosses to Drogheda—

Eight thousand blessings to Dowth of the Trees.
Peace on the earth where they may lie!
By the royal stream of the kings,
In the land of the great O'Neil.

How the Shannon Got Its Name

Many years ago, before recorded time, there was a well in Ossory that was shaded by a magic rowan tree. When the berries on the tree ripened, they dropped into the well's quiet, cool waters far below. There, the berries were eaten by the salmon that lived there. Red spots would then appear on these magnificent fish, and they received the name of the "Salmon of Knowledge."

It was not easy to capture one of these fish, for there were steep banks alongside the well and caverns underneath in which the fish could hide. However, one was occasionally caught, and the lucky fisherman became immediately gifted with extraordinary wisdom

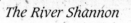

The River Shannon

and insight. Such was the case with Finn McCool, when he sampled the broiled salmon of the Boyne.

It was common knowledge that no woman could ever taste this delicacy and live until the next bright dawn. Yet Sionan, a lady noted for her thirst for knowledge, braved the danger. She believed the warning was only spread by men who wished to retain the secrets of the salmon for their own selfish male motives.

So, she went fishing and beforehand prepared everything for a magnificent feast, so sure she was of a catch. After many hours of waiting, she captured a huge fish and immediately readied it for her dinner. Hardly able to wait until it had finished baking on the coals, she reached down and took a large piece to put into her mouth. The aroma was like the most heavenly perfume, and the pink meat was delicious beyond compare. No one in this world can tell what rapture it was as a great burst of light and wisdom coursed through her mind with the first taste.

But alas! As Sionan stood by the banks of the well and enjoyed her newfound vitality, a great wave roared up from the well and became a mighty river. As the waters receded westward, they carved out a great stream and carried the unfortunate woman out to sea. Forever after, the river bore her name. Today, we know it as the River Shannon.

The Bells of Shandon

With deep affection
And recollection
I often think on
    Those Shandon bells,
Whose sounds so wild would,

In days of childhood,
Fling round my cradle
    Their magic spells.
On this I ponder
Where'er I wander,
And thus grow fonder,
    Sweet Cork, of thee;
With thy bells of Shandon,
That sound so grand on
The pleasant waters
    Of the River Lee.

I've heard bells chiming
Full many a clime in,
Tolling sublime in
    Cathedral shrine;
While at a glib rate
Brass tongues would vibrate,
But all their music
    Spoke naught like thine;
For memory, dwelling
On each proud swelling
Of the belfry, knelling
    Its bold notes free,
Made the bells of Shandon
Sound far more grand on
The pleasant waters
    Of the River Lee.

I've heard the bells tolling
Old Adrian's Mole in,
Their thunder rolling
    From the Vatican,
And cymbals glorious,
Singing uproarious
In the gorgeous turrets
    Of Notre Dame;
But the sounds were sweeter
Than the dome of Peter
Flings o'er the Tiber,
    Pealing solemnly.
Oh! The bells of Shandon
Sound far more grand on
The pleasant waters
    Of the River Lee.

There's a bell in Moscow,
While on tower and kiosk, O!
In Saint Sophia
    The Turkman gets,
And loud in air
Calls men to prayer
From the tapering summit
    Of tall minarets.
Such empty phantom
I freely grant them;
But there's an anthem
    More dear to me,—

'T is the bells of Shandon,
That sound so grand on
The pleasant waters
Of the River Lee.

by Francis Sylvester Mahony, aka "Father Prout"

The Little Green Shamrock of Ireland

There's a dear little plant that grows in our isle,
'T was Saint Patrick himself, sure, that set it;
And the sun on his labor did smile,
And with dew from his eye often wet it.
It thrives through the bog, through the brake, through the mireland;
And he called it the dear little shamrock of Ireland,
The sweet little shamrock, the dear little shamrock,
The sweet little, green little, shamrock of Ireland.

by Andrew Cherry

Saint Patrick

Longing

O the sunshine of old Ireland, when it lies
On her woods and on her waters;
And gleams through her soft skies,
Tenderly as the lovelight in her daughter's
Gentle eyes!

O the brown streams of old Ireland, how they leap
From her glens and fill their hollows
With wild songs, til charmed to sleep
By the murmuring bees in meadows where the swallows
Glance and sweep!

O my home there in old Ireland—the old ways
We had, when I knew only
Those ways of one sweet place;
Ere afar from all I loved I wandered lonely,
Many days!

O the springtime in old Ireland! O'er the sea
I can smell our hawthorn bushes,
And it all comes back to me—
The sweet air, the old place, the trees, the cows, the
thrushes Mad with glee.

I'm weary for old Ireland—once again
To see her fields before me,
In sunshine or in rain!
And the longing in my heart when it comes o'er me
Stings like pain.

by John Todhunter

Castle ruins near the sea in Northern Ireland

The Earth and Man

A little sun, a little rain,
A soft wind blowing from the west,
And the woods and fields are sweet again,
And warm within the mountain's breast.

So simple is the earth we tread,
So quick with love and life her frame,
Ten thousand years have dawned and fled
And still her magic is the same.

A little love, a little trust,
A soft impulse, a sudden dream,
And life as dry as desert dust
Is fresher than a mountain stream.

So simple is the heart of man,
So ready for new hope and joy;
Ten thousand years since it began
Have left it younger than a boy.

by Stopford Augustus Brooke

A 900-year-old oak tree

The Buried Forests of Erin

There were trees in Tir-Conal of the territories
In Erin's ancient yet remembered days,
Where now to clothe the league of bogland lonely

Is only heather brown or gorse ablaze:
Where rivers go from source to sea unshaded,
Where shine in desolate moors the scattered lakes,
And sedges only, where once were willows,
And curlews where were deer in woodland brakes.

The spades of peasants of the peat uplifting
Strike bog-black roots of oak or red or fir,
And then 't is known, here the primeval forest
Was murmurous to all winds with leaves astir,
Where to the sky's blue rim the heath unending
Lies bare, before the honey-searching bees.
O'er camping hosts, once spread the giant branches
Of oaks in autumn sounding like the seas.

There was no mountain of our many mountains,
There was no voiceful-watered purple glen,
Without its share of scarlet-berried ashes,
Without its nut-trees by the river then;
Round every dún* of every royal chieftain
White apple-boughs shook down their blossomy
showers,
And up to craggy heights like armies climbing
Went pine trees, straight as spears and tall as towers.

Fallen in Erin are all those leafy forests,
The oaks lie buried under bogland mold;
Only in legends dim are they remembered,
Only in ancient books their fame is told.

**fortress*

But seers who know of things to come have promised
Forest shall rise again where perished these,
And of this desolate land it shall be spoken:
"In Tir-Conal of the territories, there are trees."

by Alice Milligan

Am I Remembered?

Am I remembered in Erin?
I charge you, speak me true—
Has my name a sound, a meaning
In the scenes my boyhood knew?
Does the heart of the mother ever
Recall her exile's name?
For to be forgot in Erin,
And on earth, is all the same.

Oh mother! mother Erin!
Many sons your age hath seen—
Many gifted, constant lovers
Since your mantle first was green.
Then how may I hope to cherish

The dream that I could be
In your crowded memory numbered
With that palm-crowned companie?

Yet faint and far, my mother,
As the hope shines on my sight,
I cannot choose but watch it
Till my eyes have lost their light;
For never among your brightest,
And never among your best,
Was heart more true to Erin
Than beats within my breast.

by Thomas D'Arcy M'Gee

A Giant's Story

Finn McCool was a great giant of a man and, as such, he often had a great temper. Once it happened, so long ago that no one remembers when, that Finn and his neighbor got into a fine argument over who had the prettier view. Each sat on his respective mountaintop and disputed for more than a week.

Coomakesta Pass, Ring of Kerry, Ireland

Finn would argue, "How can anything compare with this scenery? I can see the valleys stretching before me, wide and green, and the mountains rising up behind me each and every morning."

His neighbor would sneer back, "Mountains and trees and grass! You call that a pretty scene? Look at mine—I don't just have the hills and valleys to look at, but I have rivers and lakes, and the ocean itself washes up against my land. Land never changes, but the water gives me something new to admire each and every day."

Now try as he might, and he tried for six days and nights, Finn could not think up an argument to counter his neighbor. It was true. Finn looked out every day and saw the same mountains and same trees and same grass growing dumbly. When Finn sneaked a peek at his neighbor's land, he saw the river calm once and then roaring after a storm, the lake deep and dark and then sparkling in the sun. And the ocean . . . well, the majestic blue water almost broke Finn's heart.

Finn became furious thinking his neighbor was right, so he flew into a rage and rushed onto the adjoining land. He took up a great handful of earth and flung it into the sea, where it landed and became the Isle of Man in the Irish Sea. And as to the hollow Finn had dug, that began to fill with water where the earth had sprung a leak. Soon Lough Neagh, the largest lake in Ireland, was formed. Finn was pleased with himself, because now he had his own body of water to gaze upon.

The Little Black Rose

The Little Black Rose* shall be red at last;
What made it black but the March wind dry,
And the tear of the widow that fell on it fast?
It shall redden the hills when June is nigh!

* *Mystical name of Ireland used in Gaelic poetry (Roisín Dubh)*

The Silk of the Kine shall rest at last;
What drove her forth by the dragonfly?
In the golden vale she shall feed full fast,
With her mild gold horn and her slow dark eye.

The wounded wood-dove lies dead at last!
The pine long-bleeding, it shall not die!
This song is secret. Mine ear it passed
In the wind o'er the plains of Athenry.

by Sir Aubrey T. De Vere

What Will You Do, Love?

What will you do, love, when I am going,
With white sail flowing,
The seas beyond?—
What will you do, love, when the waves divide us,
And friends may chide us
For being fond?

Slea Head, Dingle Peninsula, County Kerry

Though waves divide us, and friends be chiding,
In faith abiding,
    I'll still be true!
And I'll pray for thee on the stormy ocean,
In deep devotion—
    That's what I'll do!

What would you do, love, if distant tidings
Thy fond confidings
    Should undermine?—
And I, abiding 'neath sultry skies,
Should think other eyes
    Were bright as thine?
Oh, name it not!—though guilt and shame
Were on thy name,
    I'd still be true:
But that heart of thine—should another share it—
I could not bear it!
    What would I do?

What would you do, love, when home returning,
With hopes high-burning,
    With wealth for you,
If my bark, which bounded o'er foreign foam,
Should be lost near home—
    Ah! what would you do?
So thou wert spared—I'd bless the morrow
In want and sorrow,
    That left me you;

And I'd welcome thee from the wasting billow,
This heart thy pillow—
That's what I'd do!

by Samuel Lover

Tale of the Four-Leafed Shamrock

Many years ago, a magician arrived in the village of Dingle. He performed many tricks, such as eating a dozen blades of straw and then pulling a ribbon from his throat. But his best act was to harness a little gamecock to a great log of wood and have the poor creature haul it about.

Now men, women, and children would break their own bones running to see the cock, for such was the smallness of the bird in contrast to the great weight of the timber. One day, when the magician was driving the cock on a road outside the village, he met a man with a bundle of fresh grass on his back.

The man was astonished to see the crowds running after the cock, for all he saw was the small bird easily dragging a single piece of straw behind him. When he pointed this out to the people, they laughed at him.

"You fool," said the people. "Don't you see the cock drawing a great log of timber, that it would fail any horse to draw?"

"Indeed, I do not," said the man. "I see a cock pulling a little piece of straw, just as I've seen many a time at my own home."

Now the magician was listening close by, for indeed the cock was only pulling a piece of straw, and he did not want his trick found out. He thought there must be something in the bundle of grass the man had on his back that caused his sight to be made clear. So he went to the man and asked, "How much will you take for that bundle on your back, good fellow?"

The man didn't wish to sell the grass, but when the magician offered 20 pence (for just grass!), he had to make the bargain. The magician gave the bundle to his assistant and told him to throw it in the river when no one was looking.

Now as soon as the boy did this, and the bundle went down with the current, the man became as big a fool as any in the crowd. He ran with the other people to see the bird hauling the wood.

Later that day, after the man returned home, he told his wife how at first he thought the cock was only dragging a piece of straw, but then, after selling his bundle of grass, he could see that it was actually a great log of wood.

"Oh, you fool!" said his wife. "There must have been a four-leafed shamrock hidden in your grass. While you had the shamrock, every enchantment and devilment was kept from you. Now that you've parted with it, it's plain to see that you are as big a fool as the others."

"But at least I've got my money," said the man, digging into his pants pocket. But all he came out with were 20 ordinary three-leafed shamrocks, not even good enough to feed the pigs. Then he knew that his wife's words were true, and he really was a fool.

The Shannon

River of billows, to whose mighty heart
The tide-wave rushes of the Atlantic Sea;
River of quiet depths, by cultured lea,
Romantic wood or city's crowded mart;
River of old poetic founts, which start
From their lone mountain-cradles, wild and free,
Nursed with the fawns, lulled by the woodlark's glee,

And chushat's hymeneal song apart;
River of chieftains, whose baronial halls,
    Like veteran warders, watch each wave-worn steep,
Portumna's towers, Bunratty's royal walls,
    Carrick's stern rock, the Geraldine's grew keep
River of dark mementos! Must I close
My lips with Limerick's wrong, with Aughrim's woes?

by Sir Aubrey T. De Vere

Limerick, on the River Shannon

A River and a Miracle

When St. Patrick first came to Dublin, the daughter of the local king had just drowned in the river that divided the village in half. The king told St. Patrick that he would become a Christian if the holy man restored his daughter to life. St. Patrick prayed over the river, and the princess lived. Her name was Leife, and the river was thereafter called Leife's River or, as it is now known, the Liffey.

An Ancient Place

The name of County Wicklow is taken from the ancient Norse words *wyking alo,* which mean "Viking meadow." Wicklow is also nicknamed the "Garden of Ireland" because of its flower-festooned landscape irrigated by rivers and lakes. The town of Wicklow itself was founded by the Vikings in the ninth century, although there was a church on the site as early as A.D. 430.

A Nation Once Again

(Ireland's unofficial anthem)

When boyhood's fire was in my blood,
I read of ancient freemen,
For Greece and Rome who bravely stood,
Three Hundred men and Three men.*
And then I prayed I yet might see
Our fetters rent in twain,
And Ireland, long a province, be
A Nation once again.

And, from that time, through wildest woe,
That hope has shone, a far light;

** Reference to the 300 Greeks who died at Thermopylae and the three Romans who protected the Sublician Bridge.*

Nor could love's brightest summer glow
    Outshine that solemn starlight:
It seemed to watch above my head
    In a forum, field, and fane;
Its angel voice sang round me bed,
    "A Nation once again."

It whispered, too, that "freedom's ark
    And service high and holy,
Would be profaned by feelings dark,
    And passions vain or lowly:
For freedom comes from God's right hand;
    And needs a godly train;
And righteous men must make our land
    A Nation once again."

So, as I grew from boy to man,
    I bent me to that bidding—
My spirit of each selfish plan
    And cruel passion ridding;
For, thus I hoped some day to aid—
    Oh! can such hope be vain?
When my dear country shall be made
    A Nation once again.

by Thomas Osborne Davis

Irish Blessing

How sweetly lies old Ireland
Emerald green beyond the foam,
Awakening sweet memories,
Calling the heart back home.

A view over Kenmare from Tim Healy Pass

Chapter Four

A Bit o' Sport

May you be blessed
with the strength of heaven—
the light of the sun and the
radiance of the moon
the splendor of fire—
the speed of lightning—
the swiftness of wind—
the depth of the sea—
the stability of earth
and the firmness of rock.

—from "Patrick's Breastplate," attributed to St. Patrick

The Ghosts' Game of Football

Once, long ago, a poor lad named Sean was on the road looking for service when he came upon a farmer's house. Very near the house stood an old castle, black and dreary.

"God save all here," said Sean when he was let inside the door.

"God save you kindly," replied the old farmer. "Come to the fire, lad, and let me have a look at you."

Sean was only too happy to comply, for it was a terribly cold night. While warming himself by the fire, he gathered up his courage and asked, "Could you give me a night's lodging?"

"You're welcome to it," said the farmer. "Only you must sleep in a room in the old castle. Be assured we will have food and a fire and whatever you like to drink. And if we find you alive in the morning, you shall have ten pounds (£10)."

"Sure, I'll be alive," said Sean, thinking the farmer was having him on.

"Don't be too sure, my lad," said the farmer. "The place is haunted, and the six people who slept there this past year, since my father's death, did not wake. If you can banish the spirits altogether, I'll give you a good farm and my daughter's hand, if you find both to your liking."

"No need to say it twice," said Sean, for he had seen the farmer's land and figured the daughter couldn't be that bad. "I've got a good conscience and fear no evil spirit except for Old Scratch himself."

The farmer got the food and drink ready and showed Sean to the castle. There he bade him "Good night and Godspeed" in such haste that Sean didn't hear the blessing. Sean sat down on the biggest chair in the room and opened his prayer book, saying to himself, "If there's any danger, this prayer book will help me more than a tumbler of strong drink."

Soon enough, Sean heard a "thump, thump, thump" from overhead until it came to a hole in the ceiling. Then he heard someone cry, "I'll fall, I'll fall!"

"Fall away," said Sean, and down came a pair of legs with no body. Then another crackling and whacking came to the hole in the ceiling, saying, "I'll fall, I'll fall!" Sean again said "Fall away," and down came a man's body right on top of the legs. Then came the shoulders, arms, and a head with a cocked hat, and finally a whole man was standing before Sean.

Then two more men appeared, each one dressed more old-fashioned than the next. Now before Sean even had a chance to find his courage, the three old gentlemen produced a small ball and began to kick it across the

Cork Castle on the Cork River

room as fast as they could. 'Round and 'round the room it went, the man in the cocked hat playing against the other two.

"Fair play is fair play," said Sean, as bold as he could, but the words only came out as a whisper. "If you other gentlemen don't mind, I'll help you, sir."

So he joined the game and gave as good as he got, until his shirt was wringing wet with his efforts. Still the ball flew from one end of the room to the other like thunder. Not a word was said between the ghosts, and Sean was too scared to utter a sound.

At last the faint glow of dawn's light began to edge into the room, and the ghosts stopped their awful game. Sean collapsed on the chair, and the ghosts gathered around him.

"Gentlemen," gasped Sean, for he was very winded, "as the sport is over and I've done my best to please you, can you tell me what is the reason for your game here night after night?"

"We played at life," shrieked one of the ghosts, "and now are doomed to play at sport forever."

"Don't you wish to stay and play with us, lad?" screamed another ghost.

Sean's eyes grew wide, and the hair on the back of his neck stood straight, but he replied as calmly as possible. "No, sir, you tire me out too much. But is there any way I could hope to give you the rest you deserve?"

"Them is the wisest words you ever said in your life," said the ghost in the cocked hat. "Some of the six who were here before found enough energy to play with us, but at our first words, they expired. You're the first with the courage to speak, my lad."

The ghosts then explained to Sean that they were the father, grandfather, and great-grandfather of the farmer in the house next door.

"And from father to son to son, we were all too fond of money," sobbed the eldest ghost. "We lent it at ten times interest, never paid a debt we could weasel out of, and starved our tenants. Here we live with all the gold and silver we have accumulated." So saying, he pulled open a drawer in the wall to reveal coins of all kinds.

"And here are the bills and notes of those we wronged," said the middle ghost as he pulled open a drawer full of papers.

Then the ghost with the cocked hat put his cold hand on Sean's shoulder and said, "If my son wishes to avoid our fate and set us free, tell him to saddle two of his best horses for himself and you, and to ride night and day 'til every man and woman we have wronged has been set right. When that is done, we'll be at rest."

Just as these words were said, Sean could see the wall through the bodies of the ghosts, for they were fading with the coming of the day. A faint noise that sounded like "Hurry" was all that hung in the air when sunlight flooded the room. The dawn was followed quickly by the arrival of the farmer and his daughter.

They rejoiced at finding Sean alive, but the lad wasted no time on their congratulations. He quickly told the farmer to saddle two horses and—while this was being done—showed him the coins and notes. Within an hour, Sean and the farmer were on the road. And so they stayed, for three days and three nights, 'til not a single wronged person was left without his rightful farthing.

Sean took the daughter for his wife, for she was not half bad. They lived comfortably in the castle and were never bothered by spirits, good nor evil. And if ever Sean was tempted to hoard his money, or to keep a shilling that was by rights another man's, all he thought of was his game of football with the ghosts.

Tom Moody

You all knew Tom Moody, the whipper-in, well;
The bell just done tolling was honest Tom's knell;
A more able sportsman ne'er followed a hound,
Through a country well known to him fifty miles
    around.
No hound ever opened with Tom near the wood
But he'd challenge the tone, and could tell if 't were
    good;

And all with attention would eagerly mark,
When he cheered up the park. "Hark! to Rookwood,
hark! hark!
High! wind him! and cross him;
Now, Rattler, boy!—Hark!"

Six crafty earth-stoppers, in hunter's green drest,
Supported poor Tom to an "earth" made for rest;
His horse, which he styled his Old Sould next appeared,
On whose forehead the brush of the last fox was reared;
Whip, cap, boots, and spurs in a trophy were bound,
And here and there followed an old straggling hound.
Ah! no more at his voice young vales will they trace,
Now the welkin resound to the burst in the chase!
With "High over!—now press him!
Tally-ho!—Tally-ho!"

Thus Tom spoke his friends ere he gave up his breath,
"Since I see you're resolved to be in at the death,
One favor bestow—'t is the last I shall crave,—
Give a rattling view-hollow thrice over my grave;
And unless at that warning I lift up my head,
My boys, you may fairly conclude I am dead!"
Honest Tom was obeyed and the shout rent the sky,
For every voice joined in the tally-ho cry,
Tally-ho! Hark forward!
Tally-ho! Tally-ho!

by Andrew Cherry

To My Bicycle

In the airy whirling wheel is the spring strength of steel,
And the sinew grows to steel day by day,
Till you feel your pulses leap at the easy swing and sweep
As the hedges flicker past upon your way.
Then it's out to the kiss of the morning breeze
And the rose of the morning sky,
And the long brown road where the tired spirit's load
Slips off as the leagues go by!

Black-and-silver, swift and strong, with a pleasant undersong
From the steady rippling of the chain,
Half a thing of life and will, you may feel it start and thrill
With a quick elastic answer to the strain,
As you ride to the kiss of the morning breeze
And the rose of the morning sky,
And the long brown road where the tired spirit's load
Slips off as the leagues go by!

Miles a hundred you may run from the rising of the sun,
To the gleam of the first white star.
You may ride through twenty towns, meet the sun upon the downs,

Or the wind on the mountain scaur.
Then it's out to the kiss of the morning breeze
And the rose of the morning sky,
And the long brown road where the tired spirit's load
Slips off as the leagues go by!

Down the pleasant countryside, through the woodland's summer pride,
You have come in from your forenoon spin.
And you never would have guessed how delicious is the rest
In the shade by the wayside inn,
When you have sought the kiss of the morning breeze,
And the rose of the morning sky,
And the long brown road where the tired spirit's load
Slips off as the leagues go by!

There is many a one who teaches that the shining river-reaches
Are the place to spend a long June day,
But give me the whirling wheel and a boat of air and steel
To float on the King's highway!
O give me the kiss of the morning breeze,
And the rose of the morning sky,
And the long brown road where the tired spirit's load
Slips off as the leagues go by!

by Thomas W. Hazen Rolleston

Hurling: The Great Irish Pastime

"Hurling" is often considered the national sport of Ireland. A cross between field hockey, soccer, and general mayhem, the game is played with wooden sticks that are shaped like broad scythes and a ball about the same size and consistency as a baseball. The object is to send the ball into a goal or through the uprights. However, if neither of these outcomes are possible, than simply injuring as many opposing team members as possible is acceptable.

The tradition of hurling matches, pitting county against county and town against town, is centuries old. Such matches were once considered high festivals. The prettiest girl in the village was chosen as the hurling queen. Dressed in a white gown that was passed on from queen to queen, the girl led a procession of young women, pipers, and fiddlers to the hurling field.

There they were met by a procession of the young men from the village, led by the chief hurler, who was always a well-formed youth at least six feet tall. Then the chief hurler and the hurling queen would join hands and began to dance amid the cheers of the crowd.

After the opening of the hurling, the match would immediately commence and all thoughts of festivities would end as the teams got down to the serious business of beating up on each other. The matches were extraordinarily violent. Some were known to have lasted for days and to spread across the countryside with one side following the ball into another county.

Once the match had finished, the festival began again with a great supper of food, drink, and dancing. This, of course, was followed by much romance and, later, by many marriages between the young people of the neighboring villages. Thus did hurling help ensure that villages would never make actual war upon each other.

The Hurling Match

Those fairies, with all their love of gentility and the creative side of life, really dislike anything of a violent or rough nature. They particularly abhor athletic events, such as hurling and even wrestling. Many

Farmland along the coast in Mizen, West Cork

times, they attempt to end these games by some evil turn. The fairies can be quite selfish at times, or they would not interfere with Ireland's national sport.

One day, far down the coast of the Clare, a great tournament was being played between two neighboring villages. The prettiest girl of the host town, Bridget O'Mara, was already chosen as the Hurling Girl, the *Colleen-a-bhailia*. Dressed all in white, Bridget and her friends were parading to the hurling ground to preside over the match, accompanied by all the pipers and fiddlers from near and far playing lively tunes.

Little known to the festive throng that had gathered, a troupe of Sidhe, the fairies, were on the march from one fairy hill to the next. Their route would pass directly by the playing area.

The girls reached the field and were met by a procession of young men surrounding the chief hurler, Tom Finnegan by name, a lad who stood more than six feet tall. Not only was Tom a grand player, he was also the champion fiddler for the entire valley.

As was the custom, handsome Tom and beautiful Bridget held hands and began a dance, for this was how the matches began in those days. All those in attendance joined in. After the dancing, the players ran to the field, with loud shouts and shaking of their hurling sticks at each other.

Just as play was reaching its best, a great cloud of rolling dust roared along the road. The dust stopped the game, as the players and the spectators grew alarmed at the sight. "Ah, the fairies are out a-hunting and most certainly will blind us if we continue playing," they all said. As the frightened people spoke, they pointed at the towering dust cloud that blotted out the sun and hid the tops of the closest mountains. Thousands of fairies trooped past, though no eye of man, nor woman, nor elder, nor child could see them.

Tom Finnegan, a brave fellow and true, as well as a dazzling hurler, leapt up as the fairies swirled along the road. Finnegan, a fiddler of no small renown, dashed off to get his instrument and began to play his exciting tunes. "I'll get the fairies to forget about us because they will prefer to dance and make music. Soon, they'll be off to their own place to bring out their pipes and their fiddles," said Tom. Then Bridget led her handmaidens in wonderful song, and their pure voices touched the sky, causing the sun to spin, it was so happy.

With that, the whirlwind swept up the road to the fairy hill on the far side of the mountain. At last, the hurling pitch was cleared, and the play resumed safely. Everyone applauded Tom for his quick thinking, and he went on to score many points in the game. Of course, he and Bridget were blessed by the fairies for presenting their fine music and for their quick thinking that day, both being traits appreciated by the Sidhe.

As a gift, the fairies led the couple into love and blessed their resulting marriage. Never again did the fairies disrupt a hurling match whenever Tom played and his bride, the lovely Bridget, was in attendance.

Finicky Fish

An American visitor was anxious to sample the fighting abilities of the wild Irish trout. He brought his prize fly rod and picked his best trout flies. He booked a room at a farm along the River Suir, one of Ireland's best fishing waterways. The Yank carefully studied the river's riffles and pools to learn where the trout lived. Then he waited for dusk, for the trout would only rise with the coming of the moon.

Careful planning paid off. He heard the splash of a rising trout and he tried his best fly first. It bobbed merrily along the water, but not a fish looked at it. He tried other flies. No bites. He went to the pools and cast again. Still no trout expressed anything but disdain for his flies.

He returned the next night and again not a bite. Even the wonders of the fresh outdoors and the magical hills of Ireland were losing their allure. But being a fisherman means that every tomorrow is a new day. So the American was back out on the river on his last night. He was almost at the point of resorting to prayer when an elderly lady with a long pole appeared on the other side of the river.

"Much luck?" she asked.

"Nothing," the American grumbled. "I don't think these are even trout. They won't bite at anything."

"And what are you using?" asked the old woman. The American named all of his flies: the Blue Dun, the Royal Coachman, the Olive-Winged Mayfly. In desperation, he'd even tried an old Mosquito fly. With this, the woman burst into laughter.

"Sure, those are American bugs," she said. "These fish have never even seen a mosquito. Just like most

A cottage by the water in Connemara

folks around here, they're a bit thickheaded. They only know Irish bugs."

Then she cast an old piece of string into the water. On its end was tied a bit of clear fishing line and a small black gnat. A 15-inch trout rose and took it up in an instant. As the elderly lady pulled in her trophy, the American swore he'd never fish again... until his next trip to Ireland.

A Hunting Tale

A Scotsman took a young visitor from America hunting for geese on the marsh. But the fog was so thick that morning, they couldn't see the end of the gun. It was frustrating because they could hear the geese honking and rising and flying about over their heads. The mist, however, hid the birds from view.

The Scotsman thought it would be a shame for the young man to return home without having fired a shot. So he told him to fire a blind shot into the fog the next time they heard the geese rise and honk. The young man did as he was told, and a fox fell out of the sky. At a loss to explain this odd happening, the quick-witted Scot told his friend that the fog was so thick the fox was walking on it to reach the geese.

Race Day

The cross carried its message across
the winding path, down from the steeple,
where not many really listened
Because it was race day at Fairyhouse.

All the Meath men were betting
heavy coins in stained hands,
placing their hopes on Dougan's little mare
No need for church bells today.

Yet the way the race ended
there should have been more prayers
from the congregation, rain-soaked
The gelding named Joseph won.

by Martin Russell

Chapter Five

Blessings, Faith, and a Bit o' Good Luck

There's music in the Irish names—
Kilkenny... Tipperary...
There's beauty in the countryside,
From Cork to Londonderry,
And whoever makes his earthly home
Close to the Irish sod
Has found a bit of Heaven
And walks hand in hand with God.

—*Irish Blessing*

The Priest's Soul

In the olden days, there were great schools in Ireland where every sort of learning was taught to all the people. Even the poorest person in the land knew more than many of the so-called scholars of today.

At the time, there was one boy named Michael whose cleverness was a wonder to behold. Even his teachers were put to shame, for he knew his grammar and figures better than they, and he wasn't shy to show it.

Michael's greatest pleasure was in argument. He would go on and on 'til he proved to you that black was white. But if you gave in, then he would turn it all around and convince you that white was black or that there was no such thing as color in the world.

For a man like Michael, with such learning and argument in him, there was only one fit occupation—a priest. There were no real teachers back then. The priests taught the people, and Michael was a natural schoolmaster. As he proved himself to be the cleverest priest in Ireland, kings far and wide sent their children to him.

Soon enough, Michael grew very proud and forgot his beginnings in a lowly peasant's cottage. He forgot his friends and his family. And worse yet, he forgot God, who had made him what he was.

Michael loved only himself and his argument. And the pride of arguing so got hold of him, he proved there was no purgatory, then no hell, no heaven, and, finally, no God. At last, Michael proved that men had no souls at all, that they were no more than a cow or a dog or a worm, and that when they died that was the end.

"Who has seen any man's soul?" Michael asked. "Show me one and I'll believe."

No one could dispute him, and gradually all began to believe as Michael did. And since there was no heaven nor hell, nor an eternal soul to worry oneself about, everyone did as he or she pleased. In this way did Michael's teaching spread across the land.

Now the whole world was turning bad, so an angel came down from heaven and visited a very surprised Michael, for the priest had also proved that there were no such things as angels.

"You have one day to live, Father Michael," said the angel. "Prepare yourself."

Michael began to tremble and asked, "Can I have a little more time?"

"What do you need more time for, you sinner?" roared the angel.

"Oh, sir, have pity on my poor soul," said the priest.

"Oh, you have a soul then," the angel said mockingly. "When did you discover this?"

"It has been fluttering about my stomach ever since you appeared," said Michael. "I don't know why I never noticed it before."

Ruins in County Tipperary

"Indeed," said the angel. "What good was all your learning if it could not tell you that you have a soul?"

Michael bowed to the angel and asked, "Ah, good sir, now that I know I have a soul, please kindly tell me how soon I may be in heaven."

"Never," said the angel. "You denied there was a heaven."

"Well, then," said Michael, a little perturbed, "may I at least go to purgatory?"

"You have denied purgatory, as well. You must go straight to hell," was the angel's strict reply.

But then Michael smiled, for he was on his ground now, even if he was arguing with an angel. "But, my lord, I denied hell, too. So you can't send me there, either."

The angel looked a little puzzled and took some time before he answered. Then he replied: "Well, now, this is what I can do. You may live for another hundred years and enjoy every kind of pleasure and then be cast into hell forever. Or you may die in 24 hours and go to purgatory to remain until the Day of Judgment. But if you wish to enter heaven, you must find one person here who still believes in God. You will still die tomorrow, but through that belief your soul will be saved."

Michael took less than a minute to make up his mind, for now he knew he had a soul and didn't want to lose it to the devil. "I will have death in 24 hours and take my chances with heaven or purgatory."

The angel left him, and Michael ran to the school where all his scholars and students were sitting about, disputing one thing or the other. Michael called out to them, "Now, tell me the truth, and do not fear that I will contradict you. What are your beliefs? Do men have souls?"

"Father Michael," they answered one after another, "we once believed in men's souls. But you have proved it otherwise. We believe no longer. And neither do we believe in hell or heaven or God. This is our belief, for it is what you taught us."

Then Michael grew pale and cried, "I taught you a lie! There is a God, and we have immortal souls."

The shouts of laughter drowned out Michael's voice, for they thought he was only trying to provoke an argument.

"Prove it, Father," one of the students shouted. "Who has ever seen God? Who has ever seen a soul?"

The laughter grew louder, and Michael could think of no answer to the question. All his eloquence and learning, all his arguments were worthless now. He could do nothing but wring his hands and say to his students, "There is a God! There is a soul! And may the Lord have mercy on my poor soul."

The students and scholars all began to mock him, repeating his words. "Show him to us! Show us your God," they demanded.

Michael ran from them in torment, for he saw that none believed and that his soul could not be saved. In despair, he went about the country and asked everyone the same two questions: "Do you believe in men's souls? Do you believe in God?"

But the same answer came from one and all: "We believe what you have proved. There are no such things in this world."

Then Michael became half mad with fear and threw himself on the ground in a lonely place by the road. The hours were passing by, and he knew that he would die soon and face eternity alone.

Just as his last hour had begun, a small child came by the road.

"God save you kindly," the child said to Michael.

Michael bolted straight up and looked the boy in the eye. "Child, do you believe in God?" he asked.

"I have come a long way to learn about him," said the child. "Can you direct me to the finest school in this land?"

Michael's pride escaped once more and he said, "Why, the best school and teacher are close by at Father Michael's."

"Oh, not that man," the child frowned. "I am told that he denies God and heaven and hell and even men's souls because we can't see them."

"It is so," said Michael sadly.

"I would soon put a stop to such nonsense," said the child.

"How?" Michael asked in earnest, for his time was drawing to a close.

The child screwed up his face and said, "I would ask him if he believed he had a life, then he should show me his life."

"He could not do that," said the priest, "for life itself is invisible. We have it, but we can't see it or touch it."

"So if we have life, but cannot see it, then we may also have a soul, even though that, too, is invisible," answered the child.

When Michael heard these words, he fell to his knees, weeping with joy, for he knew that his soul was saved. At last he had met one person who still believed. Before he died, he told the child his story and commanded that the child should tell the others to believe. Then he laid down and peacefully breathed his last.

And wonder of wonders, with Michael's last breath, the child saw a beautiful living creature with snow-white wings mount from Michael's body and flutter around. The child ran to the school and brought back all the students and scholars and everyone from near and far. When they saw the creature, all believed that it was the soul of their teacher, and they watched with awe as it passed from their sight into the clouds of heaven.

This was the first butterfly seen in Ireland, and now all know that the butterflies are the souls of the dead waiting for the moment they may enter heaven.

But the schools of Ireland were deserted after this, for what was the use of learning from the wisest man in the country if he did not know that he had a soul and was saved only by the simple belief of a child?

The Evil Eye

If you are caught gazing at any person or thing while in Ireland, be sure to say, "God bless!" for you may be accused of giving the dreaded Evil Eye to the object of your gaze. Or if someone gives you the Evil Eye, use this prayer that St. Bridget wrote and hid in her hair for such an occasion: "If fairy, man, or woman hath over-looked ye, remember there are three greater in heaven who will cast all evil into the great and terrible sea. Amen."

To Tell the Truth

Amid the ruins of a monastery on one of the many islands dotting Ireland's western shores lies an ancient black marble flagstone. The monks who lived there hundreds of years ago gave the stone the power

A 12th-century friary in County Roscommon

of the Cremave or the Swearing Stone. From around the country, anyone suspected of a sin or crime was brought before the stone to testify to his or her actions. Even today, there are those who believe that if the accused swears falsely, the stone has the power to set a mark upon the face; if no mark appears, the person is innocent.

One time, a murder had been committed near the island. The neighbors suspected one man, but did not have proof. This did not stop them from going to the man's cottage, binding him, and taking him before the swearing stone. The people said, "If he is innocent, the Cremave will clear him. If he is guilty, let him suffer for his crimes."

The man appeared before the stone with his accusers. There they were met by a priest who said, "Speak the truth before your friends and before the face of God."

The man laid his hand upon the stone and swore that he was innocent. Instantly, his right arm shriveled up, and he fainted straight away. The stone had enacted its punishment, and the man lived as a miserable cripple to the end of his days. The people took no more actions against him for they knew that the stone would visit enough suffering on the man and his family.

A few weeks later, a daughter was born to the man and his wife. On her brow, she bore the imprint of a bloody hand. This stayed with her for the rest of her life. And every one of the murderer's descendants had a similar mark, until the seventh generation, which was born clean of the man's guilt and perjury.

The Perfect Nest

There is a little hollowed place in the cliffs that rise above the upper lakes at Glendalough in the Wicklow Mountains. This is St. Kevin's cell, where the famous

St. Kevin's Church (11th century)

saint would remove himself from the world during Lent. The cell was so small that when Kevin praised God every morning, he had to stick one arm out the window. Kevin was at such prayer one day, with his arm stretched outside, when a blackbird landed on his hand.

The bird settled herself, and since St. Kevin liked a little animal company, he went on with his prayers. The bird found his hand so warm and comfortable, she thought it was a nest. So she laid an egg in Kevin's open hand. What should a good saint do in such a predicament? He remained kneeling, with his arm extended and his hand opened, until the egg hatched and the fledgling could fly.

Historical Cheapskates

In its early years, Ireland was dotted with monasteries. During the Dark Ages, these remote abbeys served as places where learning and worship survived. But they were not immune from the ravages of warfare. Once the

Vikings discovered that the abbeys possessed gold and silver, they became ripe targets for looting.

To protect themselves from the Viking threat, the abbots constructed hundreds of high, round towers. The towers each had one entrance, about twenty-five feet off the ground. When the monks were warned of an approaching war party, they gathered themselves and their treasures into the tower, scampering up the rope ladder. Then they pulled the ladder up after them.

Round towers are among the few buildings from that era still standing intact. But, at the famous monastery of Clonmacnoise in Co. Offaly, one of the two round towers is only half complete. The story goes that one day Owen, the mason, had almost completed his work and was at the top of the tower when the monks called up to him.

"Owen," the monks shouted up, "your prices are too dear. This poor abbey can't afford to pay you."

"Holy fathers," Owen shouted down, "my prices are what they are, and your abbey has more money than the county has cows."

"If you won't lower your fee, than you shan't come down either," said the abbot. Then the monks began to remove the scaffolding.

Owen was stuck up in the uncompleted tower for a day and a night. In the morning, he called for the abbot. "Father," said Owen calmly, "I have an idea. It is easier to pull down than to build up." With that, Owen began to cast down stone upon stone. In that way, he could work his way safely to the ground.

Dunguaire Castle in County Galway

With stones landing all around them, the monks grew alarmed. They prayed for Owen to desist and told him that his price would be paid. They rebuilt the scaffolding, and Owen came down. But he refused to lay his hands on the work again. And once the story got around about how the abbey paid its bills, the tower remained unfinished.

St. Patrick Defeats the Druids

When St. Patrick returned to Ireland, he made his way to the hills of Tara, for there could be found the home of the kings of Ireland and the temples of the druids. Now this was the time of both Easter Week and the druid festival of Bealtaine. Beal was the god of new life, and no fire was to be seen in all of Ireland until the lighting of the Sun's Fire by the druids on the eve of Bealtaine.

On that night, brushwood was piled high on the peak of Tara, and the king and his court were all assembled, waiting for the hand of the high druid to strike it to flame, when someone noticed a weak but steady light from a hill to the east.

"Who has dared to light a fire before Bealtaine?" raged the king.

"Oh, King," said the high druid, "if this fire be not extinguished at once, it will never be quenched."

"Go quickly then," said the king, "to quench this fire and bring me the man who has dared to commit sacrilege. Meanwhile, light the fires of Bealtaine so that all the dwellers of Erin may rejoice in the return of the Sun's light."

And so the high druid set the brushwood pile on fire, while two other druids and the king's guards proceeded to find the man who had set the other light before Bealtaine. They soon found St. Patrick and his assistants, for it was he, of course, who set the Easter fire. The druids and guards set about trying to extinguish the fire, but they could succeed only in reducing its light but a little.

However, they did manage to bind Patrick and bring him to the king. Now when they brought Patrick before the king and his people, no one rose to show respect to the stranger, except for the oldest druid and the youngest poet of the king's court. But the king himself showed no respect whatsoever, and he spoke sharply to Patrick: "Know ye not that whoever kindles a blaze on the eve of Bealtaine, before the fire is kindled on Tara itself, is condemned to death?"

A Celtic druid with Bronze Age objects

Patrick said, "I have brought a greater light to Ireland," and he explained to the assembly about the creation and fall of man, the incarnation of the Son of God, and our redemption through Christ. He also said that no one should worship any other gods, including the life-giving Beal.

Such was the strength of his words and the fervor of his enthusiasm that many in the crowd were moved by what he said. But the heart of the king, and of most of the druids, remained hard. However, seeing that Patrick had gained the respect of many of his followers, the king ordered that lodging be made for Patrick, and he asked him to continue the argument with the druids the next day.

In the morning, thousands gathered on the plain below Tara to hear the argument. The high druid challenged Patrick in an arrogant tone, saying, "If your Son of God has redeemed the world, and if you are sent by him, work a miracle to prove your mission."

"I will not seek to disturb Providence to gratify mere curiosity," answered the saint.

"Then I will prove the truth of Beal and the druids with what you fear to attempt," said the high druid. He then began to chant spells and to wave his wand in the air. Suddenly, a thick veil of snow began to fall and shut out the light of the sun. Intense cold filled the air, and everyone's teeth began to chatter.

"You see how the people suffer," said Patrick. "Now, banish the snow and warm the air with sunshine."

"I cannot until this same hour tomorrow," said the druid.

"You are very powerful for evil," said Patrick. "Very different is the gift of the messenger of the giver of all good." So saying, Patrick made the sign of the cross and invoked the name of the Holy Trinity. Then the snow sank into the soil, the grass became green and dry, and the sun shone brightly in a clear, blue sky. All the people rushed toward the saint to obtain his blessing.

The king, however, was not convinced and wanted other proofs. He directed that the high druid and Patrick should throw their sacred books into the water of a nearby spring. "Let him in whose book the letters remain be declared the minister of the truth," said the king.

But the druid would not consent, for he claimed that Patrick had a power over water that the druid did not have. When the king suggested that the same trial be made with fire, the druid again refused to consent.

"Well," the king cried, "something must be done. Let this final trial be made. Each shall enter the tent of the other with dry boughs and set it on fire. The tent that remains will be judged the bearer of truth."

So the druid filled Patrick's tent with dry kindling. But St. Patrick appointed the young poet to fill the druid's tent with young, green boughs, so strong was his faith. By mutual agreement, the druid left his mantle in the saint's tent, and the poet placed his own cloak in the druid's tent. Both huts were fired up at the same time. In a twinkling, the green twigs in the druid's tent were burned to ash, the flames taking everything with them. Nothing was spared but the poet's cloak. In St. Patrick's hut, nothing was consumed, except for the druid's own cloth.

This was the last trial the people would suffer. Thousands, including the queen and her daughters, openly confessed their belief in the God of Patrick.

Let's Give Him a Hand

St. Aengus of Laois lived with the wild animals as a hermit before joining a monastery at Clonenagh. When living as a monk, he volunteered for the most menial chores. One day, St. Aengus found himself at one of these tasks, chopping wood. Unfortunately, his axe slipped, chopping off the saint's left hand.

Immediately, St. Aengus was surrounded by birds, all crying out in pain. But Aengus remained confident in the goodness of God. He merely picked up his severed hand and put it back on his arm. The hand was instantly reattached, and the good saint continued his chores. The less reverent have said ever afterward that St. Aengus was something of a cutup.

Sun Worshipers

As hard as it may be to believe during the frequent gales and soft days of rainy weather in Ireland, Scotland, and Wales, the ancient Celts may actually have been sun worshipers. It wasn't that the climate was any different. It was just that, as farmers and herdsmen, they depended upon knowledge of the seasons, and that meant paying attention to the passing of the sun through the heavens. Bealtaine, on the first of May, was a celebration of the coming of summer and the beginning of the growing season.

Stone circles, which probably helped the ancients keep track of the sun's voyage, can still be found scattered throughout the British Isles.

The Dingle Peninsula in County Kerry

Chapter Six

Matters of Life, Love, and Death

May you be poor in misfortune,
rich in blessings,
slow to make enemies,
quick to make friends.
But rich or poor, quick or slow,
may you know nothing but happiness
from this day forward.

—Irish Toast for the Bachelor

The Woodcutter Who Cheated Death

Donal O'Toole was a woodcutter. He scoured the forests and glens of Donegal every day, gathering enough wood to keep his master's castle warm and cozy for all inside. It was a hard job, but a worthy one. But while Donal kept at his job each day, rain or shine, his mind was never at rest. In short, he was not satisfied with his condition.

One day as Donal was trudging back to his master's castle with a full load of wood on his back, he met a young gentleman.

The young man hailed him and said, "Worthy Donal, a man can plainly see you are working yourself to the bone. Do you not tire of cutting and carrying the wood, day in and day out?"

Now this young man cut a striking figure, all dressed in black—he wore black breeches, a black cape, and a black hat as dark as moonless midnight. But Donal was too tired to notice such things, and he put down his burden to talk with the young man.

"Of course, I'm weary. Yes, weary enough, and I should be only too happy if I should see a change in my occupation," said Donal.

Then the young man turned his full face to Donal, who shuddered, for there was no face there, at least not a face like any Donal had seen before. There were only two bright-red eyes and a mouth that yawned open like a well with no bottom.

"Donal, I am Death," said the young man, "and if you throw in your lot with me, I'll make you the finest doctor in the country."

"A doctor, eh?" said Donal. "I'd like that. No cutting trees or carrying wood anymore. And I'd be my own master?"

Death's mouth formed a ghastly smile, and he said, "You'll be your own master, but with one condition. The first time you cheat me of any death that is my due, I will come for you instead."

Donal did not waste a minute to consider, for he was very tired of cutting and carrying the wood for his old master. "I accept," Donal cried, "and I don't care what conditions or contract you lay down."

"Very well," said Death. "Our bargain is complete. Now this is how you will serve me and how you will become a doctor of great renown."

Saying this, Death pulled a strange squat bottle of the grayest glass from out of his cape and gave it to Donal. As Donal looked at the bottle, Death continued, "You will be called to many a sick person's bed. Stand at the foot of the bed and look through this bottle to the head of the bed. If you see me standing at the head, you'll know that I will soon be there. But if I am at the foot of the bed, then recovery is assured."

Donal stuck the bottle in his pouch and, before he lifted his eyes back to the road, the young man was gone. Donal did not know if he had been dreaming or if he had indeed met Death, but he did know that he did not want to go back to cutting wood. So off he went, in the opposite direction of his master's castle, with the fresh-cut wood left lying beside the road.

Now, the first village he came to was a small one, with barely enough cottages to even be called a village. Out of the smallest cottage came a young woman with grief and tears on her beautiful face. "Ah, *Musha*, is there no one here who can help us?" she cried. Donal, being a soft-hearted soul and also being taken with the maiden's pretty looks, tried to comfort her.

"There, there, my little one," he said. "What troubles you so? Sure, the world is a cruel place, but all in all, it can't be that bad."

"It's my father. He had some bad meat and has been ill for three days, and now he is surely dying," the girl sobbed.

Then Donal remembered his bargain with Death and the gray bottle in his bag. "Well, I'm something of a doctor myself. Let me see your father and what ails him."

So the girl took Donal into the cottage and led him to her father's bed. Upon the bed Donal could see that the man was very ill indeed. His face was white, his blue eyes were cold, and his stomach was so fat from the bad food that it lifted the ragged blanket off the bed.

"Leave us for a minute, my darling," said Donal and motioned for the girl to go outside. After she left the cottage, Donal withdrew the gray bottle from his bag and went to the foot of the bed. Trembling, he put the bottle before his eyes and looked toward the head of the sick man's bed. There was nothing but the sick man's own slow gasps. Donal whirled about and gazed toward the foot of the bed. And there, plain to see as if the sun itself was in the cottage, stood Death.

Raising his awful face to Donal, Death said, "You have done well, my servant. You will become a prosperous man. Now take your gray bottle and fill it with any nearby water and give the sick man a few drops. He will be soon be well and on his feet to give you another reward."

As soon as Donal had done what Death said, the man's breathing became easy, and within the day he was sitting up in bed. When he heard how Donal had saved his life, the old man told Donal that he was welcome to anything he had, but added that, being a poor sodcutter, he had little.

"I ask for the only treasure that a man can have in life," Donal said, "the hand of your good daughter in marriage."

Assuring himself that his daughter agreed, which you may be sure she most certainly did, Donal being a

A cottage in County Cork

comely man himself, the old man readily gave his daughter to Donal, and they were married the next day.

After his marriage, Donal continued his services to Death throughout the country. His fame and fortune spread wider and wider, for Donal became known as the only doctor who could truly cure those at the threshold of death's door. Everyone he said would live, lived, and every person he said would die, died.

Now it happened that the old man who was Donal's father-in-law loved his meat better than he loved life, and he did not care where it came from or how it was prepared, so long as he got his taste of it every day. So sooner rather than later, the old man was sick again and took to his bed with the death fever upon him. Donal was summoned and came as quickly as he could, but all hope was gone when he arrived.

Donal went to the old man's bedside and, as before, looked through his gray bottle toward the head. When he looked, Donal saw Death at the old man's head and knew that there was nothing he could do. But his wife begged and entreated him to save her father. Donal loved his wife with a fierce love, so he came up with an idea.

He requested that the strongest young men of the village come to the cottage. When they arrived, he told them to take the old man and turn him in his bed, laying his head where his feet should be and his feet where his head should be. Knowing that Donal was the best doctor in the country, the young men immediately did as they were told. And soon the old man's health improved.

But Donal knew Death would be hard to cheat, so he kept a watch through his gray bottle, and soon enough Death began creeping down toward where the old man's head lay. Donal called for the young men and told them to turn the old man back to his original position. And so this game went on throughout the day and night, until Death became so angry that he left as fast as he could.

When the old man finally grew well again, Donal left to tend to his other patients. But he had not gone far from the village when Death met up with him.

"You are mine now, Donal," said Death in a rage, "for you have broken my condition and cheated me out of my rightful due."

"Without a doubt, that is so," said Donal, "but will you allow me a respite from death until I've said my prayers?"

Death granted his request, for Donal had been a faithful servant. Donal then turned to Death and said, "I'll never say them at all, and so my respite shall last forever."

Death left Donal in an even greater rage, vowing to have him despite his trickery. Now things continued to prosper for Donal, and Death caused him no trouble. One day, though, Donal found himself alone on a country road, where he met a young and downcast child.

Donal asked him whatever was the matter, and the child said, "I cannot remember the Lord's Prayer, and surely my mum will punish me because I've lost it."

Donal could not stand to see one so young in such agony. He took a seat at the side of the road and taught the child the prayer. No sooner had Donal said "Amen" when he turned and saw that the child was no child, but Death himself.

"I have you now," said Death gleefully, more than a little pleased with himself for the trick he'd played on Donal.

But Donal was quicker than Death knew, and he replied, "Ah, you are a wonderful fellow and surely there's no place you can't be found, be it the whole wide world or even this little bottle here." And saying this, Donal pulled out the gray bottle that Death had given him.

"That's true," said Death. "I am everywhere and in everything, and no one can deny me my due."

"Surely even you can't fit in here. Death's greatness is too big to fit in such a small bottle," Donal taunted.

"How can you doubt me, Donal?" said Death. "Here, I will prove it to you." Death gathered himself up and, like a wisp of smoke, flew into the bottle. Quick as a cat, Donal pulled out a cork cut exactly to fit Death's bottle, and he knocked it in tight, saying, "Stop you in there."

Donal had trapped Death himself. Now you'd think this would be a wonderful thing—Death trapped in a bottle. And at first, it was. People fell from roofs and, though injured, did not die. They drank poison and, though sicker than a dog, they did not pass on. Soldiers' heads were cut off in battle, but still they lived. True, each part lived separately. But they lived on, for Death had left the world.

But sooner than you'd think, everyone grew dissatisfied with a life that could not end. The old grew older still and wanted rest, the sick wanted relief from their pain, and the soldiers tired of looking about for lost arms and legs. And for Donal, with no Death, there was no need for his doctoring skills. So he was forced to go back to cutting wood. Worse yet, as the years wore on, a certain friction grew between himself and his lovely wife, who soon grew lovely no more, until they could no longer stand the sight of each other.

Eventually Donal realized that he had made a mistake in keeping Death locked away. So he opened his bag and took out the little gray bottle. Saying his prayers, he opened the bottle, and Death was let out on the world again. Donal was the first person he took, and he went gratefully.

From Fionnuala

With heaving breast, the fair-haired Eileen sang
The mystic, sweet, low-voweled Celtic rhyme
Of Fionnuala and her phantom lover,
Who wooed her in the fairy days of yore
Beneath the sighing pines that gloom the waves
Of Luggalá and warbling Anamoe—
And how he whispered softly vows of love,
While the pale moonbeam glimmered down and lit
The cataract's flashing foam, and elves and fays
Played o'er the dewy harebells, wheeling round
The dappled foxglove in a flickering maze
Of faint aerial flame; and the wild sprites
Of the storm were bound in charméd sleep—

And how the lovely phantom lowly knelt,
And pleaded with such sweet-tongued eloquence,
Such heavy radiance on his lips and eyes,
That Fionnuala, blushing, all in tears,
Breaking the sacred spell that held her soul,
Fell on his bosom and confessed her love—
And how the demon changed, and flashed upon her
In all his hideous beauty, and she sank
In fearful slumbers, and, awaking, found
Her form borne upward in the yielding air;
And, floating o'er a dark blue lake, beheld
The reflex of a swan, white as the clouds
That fringe of noonday dun, and heard a voice,
As from a far world, shivering through the air:
Thou shalt resume thy maiden form once more
When yon great Temples, piled upon the hills
With rugged slabs and pillars, shall be whelmed
In ruin, and their builders' names forgot!—
And how she knew her phantom lover spoke,
And how she floated over lake and fell
A hundred years, and sighed her mournful plaint
Day after day, till the first mass-bell pealed
Its silvery laughter amid Erin's hills,
And a young warrior found her, with the dew
Of morning on her maiden lips, asleep
In the green woods of warbling Anamoe
And wooed and won her for his blushing bride.

by John Armstrong Edmund

Alf Sheehy Sent Back to the World

Now there was a man named Fitzhugh in Tralee who made himself a great friend of the country landlords by spying on the tenants. He carried his affairs so far, he got enough small tenants evicted to give himself grass for as many as forty cows.

Within Fitzhugh's bounds was a tenant by the name of Alf Sheehy. Fitzhugh was very keen to see Alf Sheehy ejected because Sheehy's small plot lay between his own grass and the road to Tralee.

So Fitzhugh made complaint after complaint to the landlord, accusing poor Alf of poaching and destroying the lord's game. But the landlord didn't believe the accusations because he had known Alf's father as an honest man who always paid his rent. But that didn't stop Fitzhugh from spreading lies about Alf, and so a great enmity grew between the two men.

One night, by pure accident they said later, Fitzhugh's cow barn was burned to the ground, and ten cows were lost to the fire. Many in the country were sad to say it, but most believed that Alf Sheehy had lit the blaze. "Sure, he owes Fitzhugh a spite, and who else would be about burning down a barn?" the people whispered. Of course, Fitzhugh was only too willing to spread the same story himself.

Now the barn burned on a Saturday night and, as bad luck goes, Alf was away in Tralee on business and didn't return 'til Sunday morning. As he was trudging past the chapel, Mass was just letting out, and a crowd saw him pass. They began to murmur just loud enough so that Alf could hear.

"There goes Alf Sheehy, who burned Fitzhugh's barn and ran away," said one man.

"I wonder why he'd come back?" said a woman.

"Sure, it's the finger of God leading him back," said another man. "The Lord wouldn't let another be punished in the place of Alf."

Now, even though he knew he wasn't guilty, Alf hung his head in shame, for the words of his friends and neighbors cut him to the heart. Alf went straight to his cabin, where he shut the door and closed the shutters. And, whether it was from grief or sickness, he died that very day.

When he was ready to be laid out for the wake, his wife sent to a neighbor for the loan of a sheet to hang over the table, but the woman refused. "I'll not give anything for Alf Sheehy, the barn-burner," she said to the widow. "The devil may mind him for all I care."

Mrs. Sheehy's requests for help were met with the same answer wherever she turned. Alf was a good man, but it was thought that he'd done a bad thing to

Fitzhugh, and everyone was afraid of Fitzhugh. So the wake was held without decent sheets on the table.

Of course, that didn't stop the whole country from stopping in at the cabin, for anyone with Irish blood can't keep from going to a wake. They all sat down and began to eat and drink and smoke and tell stories, though usually the stories had more to tell about the teller than about the poor deceased himself.

But what a surprise this wake held for the people that came and stayed. At exactly midnight, Alf Sheehy sat straight up on the table and began to speak.

"Friends and neighbors," said Alf, "now don't fear me. I've not come to harm a person here. I just wanted to tell you that it wasn't me who burned down Fitzhugh's cow barn."

One brave man rose as if to speak, but Alf turned to him with his fingers on his lips. "Hush, let me tell my tale," he commanded and continued.

"I don't know who burned the barn" said Alf sadly, "and I'm beyond caring. You people broke my heart with your false accusations—broke my heart and killed me just as if you'd plunged a knife into my breast. But now God has given me leave to return and tell you of my innocence and take the stain from my children."

Now, Alf had a great deal more to say, but an old woman sitting in a corner rose up and said, "Alf, did you see my mother in the otherworld?"

Alf looked at the old woman with contempt. "Aye, I have, and bad luck to you that I did," he said. "She is

A small community on the Dingle Peninsula

now what she was in life: a mean-mouthed gossip who'd rather tell a dishonest tale than ever praise another's soul. And she goes about milking the neighbor's cows when she thinks no one is looking, just like you do in this world."

The people all laughed, but Alf was still angry. "I was going to tell you of the wonders I've seen since I've been dead and lived in the otherworld," he said, "but since this hag interrupted me, I can say no more."

With that, he dropped back dead and speechless, never to be heard from again. And ever since then, the old woman and her children's children have been cursed because she wouldn't stay quiet 'til they could hear what Alf Sheehy had to say about the otherworld.

Lovely Mary

When first to this country a stranger I came,
I placed my affections on a comely fair maid,
She was proper, tall and handsome, in every degree,
She's the flower of this country, and the Rose of Ardee.
I courted lovely Mary at the age of sixteen,

Her waist it was slender, and her carriage genteel;
Till at length a young weaver came for her to see,
Stole the flower of this country and the Rose of Ardee.
When I get my week's wages to the Shebeen* I'll go,
And there I'll sit drinkin' with my heart full of woe,
I'll sit there lamentin', expectin' to see
Once more my own true love, the Rose of Ardee.
Farewell, lovely Mary, tho' fled from my sight,
For you I am weepin' by day and by night,
For I fear my sweet angel I never shall see,
So adieu evermore to the Rose of Ardee.

by John Hand

A Midnight Funeral

"Arrah!" cried the auld fella. "Wid ye b'lieve this?" He leaned into his story, with all around bending an ear over their pints to hear what he had to say. The pub grew quiet as the churchyard after Christmas mass.

*pub

"It's as true as I'm alive," he said. "I heerd it from the man's own lips—may God bless him and be merciful te him! An' the Lord forbid that I should lie!"

From all corners of the bar, everybody spoke and pounded their tables, "What is it? On with the tale!"

"Did ye know Brian McGee that resides up there far beyant in Ballymichael?" the auld man asked the crowd.

Some nodded and others shook their heads.

"Well he was comin' home wan dark eve from Galway Town. 'T wis after midnight or so, maybe drawin' up to wan o'clock. He had his horse an' cart wid him, an' him strollin' along at the horse's head, smokin' his pipe and contented as a cat full o' milk. Glory be to God! When what he say afore him in the mid o' the pathway but three men carryin' a coffin. Shure, *mo leun,** his hair was standin' on end when he saw them put down their load for a much-needed rest, you kin be sure o' that. But he put the sign of the Cross on himself an' bravely marched on till he came to where them three fellas were standin' beside the casket."

"'The blissin' o' God on ye,' said Brian, speaking in Irish. 'An what's with ye out at this time o'night, at all?'

"'The same to yerself,' spoke up wan of the men. 'But we need a fourth fella to help us carry this coffin an' ask no more questions.'

"'Well, I'd be glad ta help ye,' said Brian to himself But adding to himself, 'But what'll I do with me horse 'n cart?' Auld Brian, though, was wise enough not to ask aloud 'cuz the three were rough-lookin' cobs, they were.

"to my sorrow"

"But, sorra call he had, 'cuz they right well knew what he was thinkin'. 'Yer horse 'n cart'll be here when ye return,' said another of the three, giving your man a look to sour butter.

"Well, Brian McGee helps 'em with the coffin. And sorra but it was a heavy corpse inside. 'The Lord be good to us, after all this.' Brian goes on wid' 'em till they get to the graveyard. An' then they told him he might go back to his horse and cart. 'Ah,' said Brian, 'If ye need help t' dig the grave, I'll gladly lend ye a hand.'

"'Do what yese bein' told,' growled the third man, showing his shining what teeth. 'Go, now wid' ye afore it wid be worst with ye.'

"Well, you can believe that Brian didn't have to be told twict. So he quickly wint back to his horse 'n cart. An' sure enough, there they be, in the exact place where he had left 'em."

The crowd in the pub downed their pints and were ready for more, asking who was in the coffin. "Did Brian know the men?" one asked.

"Faith," said the auld storyteller. "He did indeed, for they was his three first cousins that died long ago afore that."

"And who was in the coffin?" came another question.

"Brian's own brother that died in California that same night, as he heerd afterwards in a letter that come from his uncle in Amerikay."

The storyteller looked ever more serious. "And as I told ye earlier, I heerd all this direct from Brian McGee,

The high cross at Moone Abbey (9th century)

who's never told a lie in his life. An' Brian, God rest his soul, is now dead and buried, too."

"Amen," said the crowd and turned back to their porter...after buying the auld storyteller his round o' drink. For that is what they do in the bog country when hearing a grand tale.

by Daniel Deeney

The Outlaw of Loch Lene

Oh many a day have I made good ale in the glen,
That came not of stream or malt, like the brewing of
men;
My bed was the ground, my roof the green wood above,
And the wealth that I sought, one far kind glance from
my love.
Alas on that night when the horses I drove from the
field,
That I was not near my angel from terror to shield!

She stretched forth her arms, her mantle she flung to the wind,
And she swam o'er Loch Lene her outlawed lover to find.
Oh would that the freezing sleet-winged tempest did sweep,
And I and my love were along far off on the deep;
I'd ask not a ship, nor a bark, nor pinnace to save,
With her arm round my neck I'd fear not the wind nor wave!
'T is down by the lake where the wild tree fringes its sides,
The maid of my heart, my fair one of Heaven, resides;
I think as at eve she wanders its mazes along,
The birds go asleep by the wild, sweet twist of her song.

by James Joseph Callanan

Often-Who-Came

There was once a man who had a beautiful daughter, and many men were in love with her. Among them were two lads who came courting. One of them pleased her; the other did not. The youth she disliked was very rich. He visited her father's house often, just to see the lass and to be in her company. But the fellow she liked was very poor, and he came but seldom.

The girl's father preferred that she marry the rich boy who constantly came to see her. In an effort to advance the fellow's good cause, the father arranged a lavish dinner party and sent everyone in the village an invitation.

"Drink a drink now," says he to his daughter, "on the man you like best in this company." He waited with a smile on his face, thinking she would drink a toast to the man he liked best himself.

She lifted the glass in her hand, stood up, looked 'round, and then recited:

"I drink the good health of Often-Who-Came,
But who often comes not I also must name;
Who often comes not I often must blame
That he comes not as often as Often-Who-Came."

She sat down when she had spoken her quatrain and said not another word that evening. But the rich youth, Often-Who-Came, understood that it was not he whom the lass wanted, and he did not visit her again. So with her father's consent, she married the poor but honest man of her choice, and forever after she lived to regret it.

—Fourth or fifth century; translated by D. J. O'Donoghue, 1894

The Young Man and His Bride

Sure, but there was a wealthy fellow living near Kilkee. His son was a strong lad, who knew the whys and wherefores of the cattle. From the time he was a little boy, he had helped his father around the farm, always caring for the cows.

One summer evening, when dusk was settling about the meadow, the young man was herding the cattle to the lush pasture where they were to spend the night. Wouldn't you know, but there was a fairy fort in that field. All the locals knew about the mound and usually avoided the place, but it was getting late and the herdsman had to get his cows settled in before it got dark. Anyway, the field had the best grass in all the region, probably because of the fairy influence.

The first cow to stick its head through the gate to the field began bawling and mooing, refusing to enter. It turned and ran away. The same thing happened to the other cows, and they acted as if they were being gored by another cow. None would go into the field. But the man could not see anything and, try as he might, he could not get the herd to enter. The cows were soon scattered all over the countryside, and the man had to chase them down before he went back to the farmhouse.

The farmer also had three young servants. They were lolling around the house the next day, so the farmer told them to take the herd and drive it into the field that held the fairy fort. Along with the farmer's son, the three boys also tried and tried to get the cows to move forward. But again the animals refused, and there was much bawling and mooing.

"Now there has to be something to all this. I'll go inside the field myself to see what can be done," said the farmer's son. He climbed over the gate and entered the field. He looked around, high and low, and caught sight of a tiny little man standing off to one side of the fairy fort. The son swore at the man and prepared to hit him with the blackthorn stick he used to herd the cows.

"Wisha!" cried the little man. "Don't you be doin' that now. Put down your stick."

"But you're stopping my cattle here at the gate," responded the son. "Let them through."

"Hold off," said the fairy, for it was a fairy after all. "I'll tell you the problem. I'm badly about because I need a wife and a housekeeper. I have found such a fine woman, and I was hoping that it was she coming to my gate, but it wasn't. It was only you and those cattle. Then it was you and those three young men and the cattle again," he sputtered angrily.

"So now I'll have to go fetch her and bring some of my friends along to help carry her. She's a mortal woman and may be too heavy for us. Can you help us bring her back here? If you give me a hand, I'll be your friend for the rest of your life," promised the fairy, regaining his composure. For he saw the fine young fellow as a way of getting his bride without himself having to do the work.

The young man pondered the offer and then replied that he'd be happy to help, just so he could get his cows accommodated.

"That's fine," said the little man. "I'll not be botherin' your cattle again. Be back here in thirty minutes, when the wren calls from the bush, and you can come with us to get the woman. She's a lovely creature, wouldn't you know."

The farmer's son showed up at the appointed hour, when the wren called from the bush. The old, wrinkled fairy was there already, along with a great troupe of chattering, laughing little people, each more wizened than the next. The entire mob was on horseback, as if they were about to set off on a fox hunt. A jet-black steed had already been saddled and set aside for the young man, so he mounted and the group galloped off, shattering rainbows as they rode.

They raced over moors, swam the raging Irish Sea, leapt high atop the mountains, forded all the rivers of Ireland, and galloped deep into the valleys. The young man's horse never faltered, even though they raced faster than the wind. It was as if only seconds had passed before they were in the far north of Ireland,

The Cliffs of Moher in County Clare

where the rocks meet the moon and only the fairies know the time.

With a thunder of magic hooves, the troupe rode up to the front door of a wealthy man's home in the midst of this far-off land of forest and fields. This man had a beautiful daughter, the most gorgeous woman in all of Ireland. It was no wonder the little fairy man had sought to marry her. Several days earlier, some of the fairy's friends had put her under a spell, so she was already stricken and resting a-bed in a deep slumber. She was to die that night, so the priest had already performed the Last Rites and blessed her. The fairies were ready—they even brought one of their own to replace the girl after they took her with them.

"Just go inside the house and take out the girl. We have many friends there, waiting and watching," said the fairy.

The farmer's son entered the darkened mansion—for it was the middle of the night—and crept up to the girl's bedroom. From the whispering and rustling all around, he knew other fairies were about and that it wasn't simply the night breeze fluttering the curtains. He picked up the girl, whose form was as slight as a feather. He carried her downstairs without any trouble—and nary a stair board creaking—and put her on his horse.

"Well done," said the old fairy, rubbing his hands and smacking his lips at the thought of having this beautiful girl as his wife. And off they rode again, back to the fairy fort.

When everyone arrived in a cloud of stardust, the fairy demanded that the young man give him the girl. But he was grieved to do so, fearing for the maiden and the fact that she would be living with the old fairy for the rest of her days. "No, I will not hand her over. I will keep her myself," he said, as the fairies howled and grumbled and moaned.

They were very angry at the young man and swore to take revenge. But he remained brave and steadfast, ignoring the fairies' threats. He left immediately, taking the comely young girl with him. Of course, when she awoke, she fell in love with the young man because he was quite handsome—as well as caring, considerate, and a good kisser. As you can believe, they were married in less than a fortnight.

The lad's father, as you recall, was very wealthy. But the fairies went after him, changing that almost overnight. Once the older man had fifty cows. Soon they were all driven off or dead and dying of fairy spells. The fairies ruined the crops, turned the milk, dried up the apple trees, and generally caused a terrible ruination. The farmer and his family quickly became very poor, with hardly a shilling to their name.

The young man and his new wife were quite distressed. "If my parents knew about this, they could help," she said, pursing her soft red lips in thought. So the young man took off and journeyed to the far north of Ireland to find her mother and father. Of course, it took much longer than it had before because he no longer rode the fairy horse but had to ride the family's last donkey. It was an ugly old beast that had yet to be carried away by the fairies because of its ill temper.

Tired and hungry, he finally arrived at his in-laws' home. It was a grand house, surrounded by vast herds of cattle and dozens of milkmaids and herdsmen to care for the cows.

The mother-in-law was in the front room weeping, when the young man entered the house. "Ah, since you are a stranger here you probably don't know that my daughter is dead. Her father has been laying a-bed, as well, since she died all those long days ago," the woman groaned.

"Your daughter is still alive," said the handsome visitor. "She is well and living with me as my wife."

"Hush with that talk or I'll get my husband up and after ye," she replied and called for the fellow to get out of bed and toss out the young upstart. But the young man was able to turn her anger when he told her things that only a mother would know about her daughter. Even the father-in-law was finally satisfied.

They sent for the local priest, who agreed to write to the parish vicar where the young man lived. "He'll confirm the true story," said the priest. "I'll wait," said the young husband who had thoughtfully saved the girl from the fairies.

Now this wealthy man had three strapping sons, in addition to his beautiful daughter. They didn't want to delay, waiting the days it would take to hear the reply from the second priest. So they decided to ride off and find their sister straightaway. She met them at the door of her new home, and naturally there were many hugs and kisses all around during the happy reunion.

All four then mounted fresh horses and rode back to the far north of Ireland. There was a great feast upon their arrival, as the young couple embraced and danced through the night.

The three brothers and the father-in-law inquired of the young man what livestock he had lost because he stood up to the fairies. "Fifty cows, four horses, a hundred hens and four roosters, five sows, two dogs, seven geese, and one cat," he responded.

The three brothers then took seventy of their strongest servants and friends and rode back to the field with the fairy fort. They swore they would dig up the fort, even if the old fairy was fifty fathoms below the surface of the ground.

They began digging, and it wasn't long before they had a great pit yawning before them. At the bottom of the pit was a huge flat stone, so the men began prying it up with their crowbars.

Out popped the frightened fairy, for the stone was the roof of his home. "Please leave my house be. Don't tear it away—it is the only shelter I have," he cried aloud, starting to weep. "I still have no wife, and now I'll have no house. Oh, woe is me."

"We'll stop as soon as you promise you'll give back to our brother-in-law what you stole from him. And you must promise never to bother his family again," said the three angry brothers.

"Of course, I'll do that. Just leave my poor house alone. And I'll add this bag of gold to have you know that I am acting in good faith. I'll never take even a drop of milk from any of his cows," the fairy promised, pinching his face and pulling on his white beard.

Forever after, it was thus. And the fairy eventually became great friends of the young man and his bride, the one that was almost his.

The Wedding of the Clans

I go to knit two clans together,
Our clan and this clan unseen of yore,
Our clan fears naught; but I go, oh, whither?
This day I go from my mother's door.
Then, redbreast, singest the old song over,
Though many a time hast thou sung it before;
They never sent thee to some strange new lover

To sing a new song by my mother's door.
I stepped from my little room down by the ladder—
The ladder that never so shook before;
I was sad last night, to-day I am sadder,
Because I go from my mother's door.
The last snow melts upon bush and bramble,
The gold bars shine on the forest's floor;
Shake not, thou leaf; it is I must tremble,
Because I go from my mother's door.
From a Spanish sailor a dagger I bought me,
I trailed a rosebud our gray bawn o'er;
The creed and the letters our old bar taught me;
My days were sweet by my mother's door.
My little white goat, that with raised feet huggest
The oak stock, thy horns in the ivy frore;
Could I wrestle like thee—now the wreaths thou tuggest!—
I would never move from my mother's door.
Oh, weep no longer, my nurse and mother;
My foster-sister, weep not so sore;
You cannot come with me, Ir, my brother—
Alone I go from my mother's door.
Farewell, my wolfhound, that slew MacOwing,
As he caught me and far through the thickets bore,
My heifer Alb in the green vale lowing,
My cygnet's nest upon Loma's shore.
He has killed ten Chiefs, this Chief that plights me,
His hand is like that of the giant Balor;
But I fear his kiss, and his beard affrights me,

And the great stone dragon above his door.
Had I daughters nine, with me they should tarry;
They should sing old songs; they should dance at my door.
They should grind at the quern, no need to marry!
Oh, when shall this marriage day be o'er?
Had I buried, like Moirín, three fates already,
I might say, three husbands, then why not four?
But my hand is cold, and my foot unsteady,
Because I was never married before!

by Sir Aubrey T. De Vere

A May Love Song

It is far and it is far
To Connemara where you are,
To where its purple glens enfold you
As glowing heavens that hold a star.
But they shall shine, they yet shall shine,
Colleen, those eyes of yours on mine;
Like stars that after eve assemble

And tremble over the mountain line.
Though it be far, though it be far,
I'll travel over, to where you are,
By grasslands green that lie between
And shining lakes at Mullingar.
And we shall be, we yet shall be
Oh Colleen lonely, beloved by me,
For evermore on a moor of Mayo,
Mid heather singing like the sea.

by Alice Milligan

The Cattle Jobber With One Good Eye

A cattle jobber was heading to the fair near Awnascawil when he came across a troupe of fairies dancing and partying along the way. He fell in with the company after drinking some of their magic mead, and he soon found himself on the road to a lonesome pasture where there was a great fairy fort. They entered the fort through a hole in the ground, like a burrow into a badger's house. Once inside, the jobber saw that it was a grand palace with thick tapestries and vast amounts of gold and jewels strewn about in confusion.

The company drank and ate long into the night, and the jobber joined them, eating as heartily as the rest. As morning dawned, they departed their underground castle, leaving only the jobber and their piper behind them. "Don't let this man out of your sight," the fairies warned the piper as they left.

The jobber noticed that when they were heading away, they all dipped their fingers into a box that was laid by the door and rubbed their eyes. When the jobber figured the fairy host was indeed far enough away, he decided to take on the piper and make his getaway. So he pulled up his boots and ran his fingers through his rumpled hair to make himself presentable to the outside world.

"What are you up to?" asked the fairy piper.

"I'm leaving here because I've been down below long enough," replied the jobber.

"Not at all," said the piper, rising from his bench and approaching the cattle jobber. "You won't be going anywhere."

With that, the two began wrestling, and all the furniture in the hall was upturned and the tapestries

On Ballinskelligs Bay, Ring of Kerry, Ireland

torn from the walls. During the fight, the jobber knocked the piper head over heels and broke his back on a chest of diamonds and emeralds.

The jobber then ran for the door, dipped his fingers into the box and rubbed one eye just as he had seen the fairies do earlier. Immediately, he could see all the fairies in the world 'round about him with the one eye that had been rubbed. But the other eye was blind to the fairies, though it could see everything else.

The jobber continued for two more days on his way to the fair and then stopped for the night in a house, where he asked for a drink.

"You're welcome to it," said the woman of the home. "But I need to go to the barn and get some milk. Something is the matter with our child. Since two days before yesterday, he's been screeching and hollering so that neither I nor my husband have been able to get any sleep or do our daily chores."

"I'll look after the baby while you milk the cows," said the jobber, settling down by the cradle to rock it. He noticed that the crying was not that of an ordinary child, so when the woman left the room, the jobber peeked under the blankets. Sure enough, it wasn't a baby there. It was the fairy piper whom the jobber had bested in the wrestling match three days earlier.

The wife and her husband were very young and this was their first child, so they hadn't known the difference in the crying.

"Why are you here, you rascal?" roared the jobber when he saw the fairy in the cradle.

"Oh, after you broke my back, the other fairies turned me out of the fort because they thought I could no longer play the pipes," the crippled fairy lamented. "So they put me here and took the real child back with them."

"Well, hold your tongue and give the good people who live here a chance to sleep and do their chores," warned the jobber.

"Ouch, it's the rocking that hurts my back and causes me to cry. Don't expose me now because I have no other place to go until I heal," pleaded the injured fairy.

"Then be quiet or I'll tell these people all about you," said the jobber. So the changeling was quiet again.

When the woman came back, she wondered why the child was not crying.

"I told him he'd be in great trouble if he didn't stop hollering," said the jobber. "I guess that frightened him into being still." Both the woman and her husband were glad for the peace and quiet, and they invited the jobber to spend the night. He agreed to keep watch all through the wee hours so the couple could get some sleep.

About midnight, the jobber was getting sleepy, so he asked the piper to play a tune to help him stay awake.

"It's difficult for me to play, with my back and all," replied the piper. "But I'll try if you bring me my pipes. They are above the fireplace in the loft."

The jobber retrieved the pipes and handed them to the piper, who began to play. The music was sweet and wonderful, so fine it could have raised the dead and set them to dancing. The music woke the wife and husband, who came down to the kitchen.

"Who was that playing?" they asked. "'Twas I," said the jobber. "I often play the pipes when I am traveling. It keeps me company." The fairy piper hid under his covers so the couple couldn't see that it was actually him who had been playing.

The next morning, the good woman brought in several loads of turf for the fire and then went outside again to do her chores. The jobber told the piper that he was going to throw him into the fire to get rid of him.

"That will make the fairies return the proper baby to its rightful place," said the jobber.

He went to the door to see where the woman went, but she was nowhere to be found. When he turned back, the fairy piper had vanished, leaving only his clothes.

The jobber was quite frightened then, fearing that he would have to answer for the child's disappearance. Of course, when the mother came back, she did wonder what had become of the baby.

So the jobber told her everything from start to finish, and they went outside to search for the missing fairy. Outside by the gate, they were surprised to see the real child. Naturally, everyone was glad that the baby had been safely returned.

The jobber bid the family good-bye and left the farm, continuing on down the road to the fair. On his way, he again encountered the same fairy band, seeing them through his enchanted eye. A great horde of them were in the fields, tearing up potato sprouts and ruining all that stood in their way.

"Shame on you," he cried, shaking his fist at them. "All you do is cause more trouble."

One fairy recognized the jobber and ran over to him. He poked his finger into the man's magic eye, blinding the jobber on this one side. The fairy returned to the mob and said, "Do you remember the man who turned on us and injured our piper?"

"Yes," they responded. "Well," the one fairy went on. "That was him over there on the road. I went and took

the sight from his eye, so he'll never see us again."
Which is exactly what happened, and the jobber went through the rest of his life with only one good eye, never again seeing a fairy.

Philandering

Maureen, *acushla**, ah! why such a frown on you!
Sure, 't is your own purty smiles should be there,
Under those ringlets that make such a crown on you,
As the sweet angels themselves seem to wear,
When from the pitchers in church they look down on you,
Kneeling in prayer.
Troth, no, you needn't, there isn't a drop on me
Barrin' one half-one to keep out the cowld;
And, Maureen, if you'll throw a smile on the top o' me,
Half-one was never so sweet, I'll make bowld.
But, if you like, dear, at once put a stop on me
Live with a scowld.
Red-haired Kate Ryan?—Don't mention her name to me!
I've a taste, Maureen darlin', whatever I do.

**the pulse (of my heart)*

But I kissed her?—Ah, now, would you that same to
me?—
Ye saw me! Well, well, if ye did, sure it's true,
But I don't want herself or her cows, and small blame
to me
When I know you.
There now, *aroon**, put an ind to this strife o' me
Poor frightened heart, my own Maureen, my duck;
Troth, till the day comes when you'll be made wife
o' me,
Night, noon, and morning', my heart'll be bruck.
Kiss me, *acushla*! My darlin'! The life o' me!
One more for luck!

by William Boyle

The Last Desire

When the time comes for me to die
To-morrow, or some other day,
If God should bid me make reply,
"What wilt thou?" I shall say:

the secret (of my heart)

O God, thy world was great and fair!
    Have thanks for all my days have seen;
Yet grant me peace from things that were
    And things that might have been.
I loved, I toiled; throve ill and well;
    Lived certain years, and murmured not.
Now give me in that land to dwell
    Where all things are forgot.
I seek not, Lord, thy purging fire,
    The loves re-knit, the crown, the palm;
Only the death of all desire
    In deep, eternal calm.

by Thomas W. Hazen Rolleston

An Irish Toast

Health and long life to you.
The wife (or husband) of your choice to you.
A child every year to you.
Land without rent to you.
And may you be half-an-hour in heaven
before the devil knows you're dead.

Girl of the Red Mouth

Girl of the red mouth,
Love me! Love me!
Girl of the red mouth,
Love me!
'Tis by its curve, I know,
Love fashioneth his bow,
And bends it—ah, even so!
Oh, girl of the red mouth, love me!
Girl of the blue eye
Love me! Love me!
Girl of the dew eye,
Love me!
Worlds hang for lamps on high;
And thought's world live in thy
Lustrous and tender eye—
Oh, girl of the blue eye, love me!
Girl of the swan's neck,
Love me! Love me!
Girl of the swan's neck,
Love me!
As a marble Greek doth grow

To his steed's back of snow,
Thy white neck sits on thy shoulder so,—
Girl of the low voice,
    Love me! Love me!
Girl of the sweet voice,
    Love me!
Like the echo of a bell,—
Like the bubbling of a well—
Sweeter! Love within doth dwell,—
    Oh, girl of the low voice, love me!

by Martin MacDermott

The Tinker of Ballingarry

Jack was a poor tinker who lived in Ballingarry, a village in County Limerick, many generations ago. He was not as bad off as some of the other tinkers in the neighborhood because he had a small garden behind his cottage and a grand apple tree near the well. Jack traveled the countryside most of the year while repairing pots and pans. While on his journeys, he left his wife to care for the house and garden.

One day, Jack met a very handsome fellow on the road and greeted him warmly. The stranger appreciated this on the part of Jack and replied, "I will give you three wishes. You can have whatever you want, but think carefully because you will never have this chance again."

Jack thought hard and eventually said, "I have an old armchair in my kitchen. Whoever comes to visit sits in that chair, and I have to stand. I wish that whomever sits in the chair from this time on will not be able to rise until I give him leave."

"Granted," said the man. "Now go on with your second wish, and I'd suggest you seek something that will be of service, something that will do you good."

The tinker thought some more. "Behind my house, near my well, is a tree that has marvelous apples. But all the small boys and thieves passing by try to steal every one of them. I never have one to eat. I wish that every person who attempts to take my apples be fastened to them, and the apples to the tree, so the person is stranded there until I free them."

"Good enough," said the wayfarer. "Now this is your third wish and last opportunity. I warn you for the last time to wish for something of service. Be careful now."

After some time, Jack said, "My wife has a leather bag. In it, she puts scraps of wool that the neighbors give her after she does their cleaning. All the boys in the county come and kick this bag around and pull out the wool and throw it away. I wish that everything that is placed in that bag stays there until I allow it out."

"Granted the wish," said the mysterious man. "But I don't think you chose very well." He went on his way and Jack went on his, still as poor as ever.

A year later, Jack was injured on his travels and was at home slowly recovering. But since he could not work, he and his wife were almost dead from hunger. One morning, Jack heard a knock on the door and hobbled over to answer it. A stranger stood there, looking very dark and grim.

"I see, Jack, that you are extremely poor and about to die. I've come to make a bargain with you. I will give you comfort now and make you a rich man if you will come with me at the end of seven years."

"This is quite interesting," said Jack. "But who are you?"

"Ah, Jack, I am the devil," responded the stranger, looking more dark and more grim.

Jack wasn't afraid. After all, seven years is a long time. So he agreed to the bargain, promising to go with the devil at the end of seven years.

The devil went away and, as promised, Jack became very rich. He always had food in his house, and there were plenty of coins to buy his wife a new shawl or to get a new cow for the milking. Jack no longer had to work, but he continued to roam the countryside fixing pots. But it was for his own pleasure that he did this. His wife did not need to go wool-gathering any more, much to the surprise of the neighbors.

Jack forgot about his bargain with the devil, and he was quite surprised when the fellow showed up on his doorstep on the last day of the seven years, which had passed very quickly. "Are you ready, Jack? It is now time to come with me," said the devil, quite pleased that he had another soul to take.

"A promise is certainly a promise," replied Jack. "I'll go along with you without a fuss. Just let me pack a few things. I'll be right back, but until then, please sit in my armchair in the kitchen until I return. I want to say good-bye to my wife."

The devil, being tired, sat down in Jack's comfortable chair and waited. When Jack came back to the kitchen, he told the devil that he was ready to go.

The devil tried to rise but could not. He pulled, he jerked, he kicked, he roared, he yelled, but nothing worked. He was stuck fast to the chair. Seeing that he could not escape, he said to Jack, "I offer you twice as much fortune, and I'll come back in fourteen years. Then, off we will go together."

That sounded good to Jack, so he gave the devil leave from the chair. The devil shot out of the house like lightning and was not seen again... for fourteen years. During that time, Jack did right well for himself, even better than before, although he never bragged or made much ado about his growing riches.

When the time was up, there the devil appeared again. He was very cautious this time and said to Jack, "No tricks now. Let us go."

Jack was ready to leave but asked to take one last look at his house, his apple tree, and his garden. The devil agreed, and the two went for a walk around the property. After spotting the tree with its large, juicy apples, Jack suggested that the devil pick some fruit for their journey. "You can reach them easier than I can. So help yourself," the tinker suggested.

At that, the hungry devil reached up to pick an apple. But he could neither pull the apple from the tree, nor could he let go of the fruit. He swung back and forth, yelling and screeching for Jack to let him go. "Get me down from here, you trickster!" roared the devil.

"I will not," replied Jack, sure of himself. "There's no reason for me to release you, and I'd rather have you swinging there for all eternity. It's all the same to me."

"All right, all right," sputtered the red-faced devil, who was having quite a time catching his breath while hanging there on that hot day. "I will give you three times the riches you have now and twenty-one years in which to enjoy it all. Just loosen me from this tree."

Jack considered this offer and agreed to the bargain. He didn't quite trust the devil hanging around his backyard for all eternity, anyway, thinking that the fellow could be up to all sorts of mischief for that time. So he let the devil go and away he went, faster than before.

Ocean inlet and coastal marshland in Galway

From that day on, Jack never wanted for anything. He was wealthy beyond even his dreams, although he kept living in his cottage and never showed off his riches to anyone.

But even the best of times come to an end. The twenty-one years flew past, and again the devil showed up at the door. "I'm on to all your tricks, so don't try anything on me," he warned.

"Just let me say good-bye to my wife one last time," asked Jack, and the devil warily agreed.

When Jack returned, he was carrying the bag in which his wife once collected her wool. "When I was a boy, I used to jump in and out of this bag when playing with the other children in the village. But that was a long time ago, when I could move much faster. Now I am old and heavy and can't use my bag like that. But I would like to take it with me, as a reminder of my youth." And he showed the bag to the devil.

"That jumping in and out of the bag is not much of a trick at all," scoffed the devil, taking the bag from Jack and looking it over. "Well," said Jack, "you try it then. I won't believe that you can do it until I see you jump in and out."

The devil accepted the challenge and sprang inside. Jack closed the bag immediately and tied it shut. Oh, the devil howled and punched and kicked but could not get out of the bag. Jack slung it over his back and walked out onto the road. In a nearby field, he spotted six brawny farmhands threshing grain with their flails.

"My bag is too thick and heavy for me to carry," he said to the men. "Could you please hit it a few times for me to limber it up and make it easier to drag along?" The men obliged, giving plenty of good wallops to the bag. With each blow, it rolled around and jumped about like it was alive. Naturally, there was plenty of screeching from the angry devil inside who was getting quite a pounding.

"You must have the devil himself in there, making such a racket," one of the men said, giving the bag another mighty blow. "Sure enough," laughed Jack, "now wouldn't that be grand if it was!" At that everyone had another great chuckle and whapped the bag again for good measure.

Jack picked up the bag after thanking the men for their help and staggered off down the road, for the devil was plenty heavy. At every step, the devil pleaded to be released. Jack refused. "Never again will I let you out to cause trouble in the world. You've done enough. I'll pay you for your work."

With that, Jack kept walking until he came to a grist mill, with its huge wheels grinding the grain into flour. He asked the miller if he could toss his bag into the mill, and the man agreed. Again, there was howling and crying as the bag and the devil were crunched and flattened and ground. "My," said the miller, "you certainly have the devil wrapped up in that bag." "Sure and you're right, grind on, Mister Miller, grind on." And so he did.

When the miller was finished, Jack picked up the flattened bag and kept walking. By this time, the devil was in pretty bad shape and could only utter a few snarls and moans. It wasn't long before Jack came to a blacksmith, who was pounding out wheel rims on a great anvil. Several helpers were also banging away with their hammers on some plows. "Gentlemen," asked Jack, "could you give a few whaps on the bag for me with your hammers? It needs to be pounded out flat and smooth, so I can more easily carry it." The smiths each gave several good raps on the bag, and every time the devil moved inside it. Every time they hit the bag, another screech would be let out and it would jump around some more.

"Why does it hop around so?" asked the smiths. "I'm giving the devil his comeuppance," said Jack. That sounded good to the men, so they all hit the bag at least ten more times each.

For good measure, one smith took a glowing rod from the fire and poked the bag, burning a hole in its side. The hot iron bar went into the devil's eye, and he squealed and hollered some more.

"Free me, you fiend, you've blinded me!" cried the devil. "I swear I'll never bother you again. I will not have you in my underworld. I'll leave you alone forever. I'll give you even more riches—four times what you've had before—if you let me out."

With the hole in the bag, Jack figured that the devil would find a way to wiggle out sooner or later. So he agreed to the bargain and released the devil, who could barely crawl away, he was in such a state.

So Jack went home a happy man. He was free from his bargain with the devil and lived happily until the end of his life. But he spent all his money, and by the time he was an old man, he was as poor as he was in his youth.

His day of reckoning came at last. He went to the Golden Gates of heaven and knocked on the door. "Go away," came the answer. "Go to the fellow for whom you worked all your life. Begone." Well, Jack had to leave, of course, and he figured he might as well go down to see his old nemesis, the devil.

Jack knocked at his gate, the echo ringing. "Who's there?" came a growly voice from inside. "It's me, Jack the tinker from Ballingarry," he responded.

"Oh, don't let him in. He put out my eye. He pounded me something fierce. He's a terrible trickster. If you let him in, he will destroy everything we have. Go away!" the devil yelled when he heard who was waiting to enter.

So Jack went back to heaven to try again. He was not allowed to enter, but was told to wander the world forever and carry a small lantern when the darkness came at night. Jack was never to have any rest, but was doomed to stray over the bogs, marshes, and lonely places for all eternity. He is still roaming the world and will until the Day of Judgment. Now and forever, he is called Jack O'Lantern.

The Wind on the Hills

Go not to the hills of Erin
When the night winds are about;
Put up your bar and shutter,
And so keep the danger out.
For the good-folk whirl within it,
And they pull you by the hand,
And they push you on the shoulder,
Till you move to their command.
And lo! you have forgotten
What you have known of tears,
And you will not remember
That the world goes full of years.
A year there is a lifetime,
And a second but a day;
And an older world will meet you
Each morn you come away.
Your wife grows old with weeping,
And your children one by one
Grow gray with nights of watching,
Before your dance is done.
And it will chance some morning

You will come home no more;
Your wife sees but a withered leaf
In the wind about the door.
And your children will inherit
The unrest of the wind;
They shall seek some face elusive,
And some land they never find.
When the wind is loud, the sighing
Go with hearts unsatisfied,
For some joy beyond remembrance.
For some memory denied.
And all your children's children,
They cannot sleep or rest,
When the wind is out of Erin
And the sun is in the West.

by Mrs. Clement Shorter

A scenic view in County Galway

Chapter Seven

Animal Tales

May the lilt of Irish laughter
Lighten every load,
May the mist of Irish magic
Shorten every road,
May you taste the
sweetest pleasures
That fortune e'er bestowed,
And may all your friends remember
All the favors you are owed.

—Irish Blessing

Pool of the Dragon

Many generations ago, a dragon lived in the pool near the stone bridge of Thuar. With its flame and claws, it destroyed all the territory between Duffey and Kilmeashil and as far out as Moghurry. This dragon was so strong that it sucked a team of horses into its throat by merely drawing in its breath five miles distant. The king of this country did not know what to do.

Finally, he sent his fastest runner to the court of the High King of Ireland, who lived in Munster, to plead for some great warrior to come and destroy the wicked dragon. For soon it would not leave a horse or cow or chicken or family alive on this side of the Slaney.

Off dashed the messengers, who naturally had many adventures on their way to the court, but no time can be had now to tell of them all. But even the High King was unwilling to help when told of the predicament. He feared losing any of his best and most able fighters. However, the war-blood of the Irish was never wanting. So three brave knights—O'Brien, O'Farrel, and O'Kennedy—volunteered to rescue the far-off nobleman and his kingdom.

One of these, I won't say which, was impatient to set forth. "If I can't go first," he shouted, "I will roar and roar and pound my spear upon my armor until allowed." So the High King bade him leave and hosted a great dinner in his honor the night before the three men were to depart. Pity it was that the proud warrior partook of too much mead that eve and was in no shape to go anywhere the next day.

But there was a younger brother of his abiding in the High King's castle. He was a great hunk of a fellow, but one not used to fighting. He felt more at home with the cattle, as a herdsman. Well, that lad was still brave and did not want disgrace to fall upon his father nor the name of his father's father. So he came to the High King and said, "My family will be dishonored for eternity if your excellency does not allow me to go in place of my brother."

The High King looked at the boy with pity, fearing the worst if he let him go forth. But since the strong young fellow appeared very determined, the High King waved him off with his blessing. "Well, go in God's name. David did kill the giant Goliath with a very small stone. You may be as lucky."

So off they went, the boy and the two knights. They traveled over mountains and traversed deep valleys. They eventually came to Bullawn-a-Rinka, high atop the Coolgarrow hill. They opened their spyglasses and looked over to the pool where the dragon lay digesting a meal of unfortunate soldiers who had stumbled into his path.

The rolling hills of Ireland

"Now," said the boy, "if you let me go into battle first, it will be no great loss if I fall." But his companions, honorable as they were, would not allow this. So they cast lots to determine who would venture out first. To be sure, the young man won the toss, and he was given the chance to prove his mettle.

Said he, "Help me while the vile creature is asleep." They cut down trees and burned them, making enough blackened logs for a full sack of charcoal.

The boy then climbed into the sack, carrying a sharp knife with him. Before they closed the top of the sack, he told his companions to go to the top of nearby Mount Leinster. "If you see smoke by the pool after three hours, light a fire. That will signal the countryside that the devilish dragon is slain. Then get across the bogs as quickly as possible to tell the High King what has happened," he said.

So they got themselves off to the mountain just before the monster awoke. As they clambered up the cliff, they looked back. The dragon stretched itself and began to snuff about, turning its great green head toward Coolgarrow. With that, the beast began to suck air, and the sack was picked up off the ground, headed straight toward the monster's open mouth. However, the bag with the lad inside hit the dragon with such force it knocked it down. The taste of the charcoal was not to its liking, so the beast swallowed it whole.

When the boy found himself inside the dragon, he pulled out his knife and slashed the beast's innards. The dragon had no idea what was happening but could only feel the pain in its belly. It rose up and staggered over to the pool, where it fell in and died just as the boy cut himself free. The youth then lit a fire on the shore and saw that his companions in the mountain did the same. Soon, all those around knew that the dragon was dead and the youth was alive. The knights ran off to tell the High King that the mission was successful.

The brave boy was very devout, thanking God for his victory. He decided to build a church out of gratitude and prayed that he would be shown a proper place for its construction. That night, before leaving on his return trip to the High King's castle, the young man had a dream about a duck and a drake flying along the pool.

The birds flew across Thuar Bridge and over the hill to Templeshamboo, where the duck lighted on one side of the water and the drake on the other. The boy awoke and thereafter built a monastery on the drake's side and a nunnery on the other, where the duck had found refuge. And so the ruins of these buildings can still be seen today.

Of course, the youth was well rewarded by the High King for his valiant efforts. And as for the drunken brother, there is no need to continue this tale. Needless to say, he was proud of his brother and went on to redeem himself in many battles.

The King of the Cats

The Irish have a legend that ensures their cats will be well treated. For the common household cat may be the King of the Cats, a cat with magical powers. Since there is no distinguishing mark of his rank, it is difficult to verify any cat's royal standing. The best way is to cut off a tiny bit of ear. If your cat is really the King of the Cats, he will immediately speak out and tell you some very disagreeable truths about yourself.

One Irishman, furious because the milk for his morning tea was missing again, cut off the head of the family cat and threw it on the fire. While the flames licked at its fur, the head exclaimed, "Go tell your wife that you have cut off the head of the King of the Cats. But I shall come back and be avenged for this insult."

One year later, as the same master was playing with the family's new pet kitten, it suddenly flew at his throat and bit him so severely that he died the next day.

The Lad on the Blue Horse

There once lived a farmer's wife named Maeve, who was good as gold to all her kin and neighbors. One fine day, she and another woman were out in the fields cutting oats when a large, yellow frog struggled to get out of the way of Maeve's sickle.

Upon seeing that the frog could not leap like an ordinary frog, pity arose in Maeve's heart. "There, there, you poor clumsy thing," she said.

But the other woman had no pity for the frog. "Oh, the nasty beast," she said. "If it comes my way, I'll put the point of my sickle through it."

"No!" said Maeve. "The poor creature is only crawling about trying to gather her portion of life like the rest of us." With this, Maeve reached down and gently laid the frog out of danger.

A few days later, there came a lad riding a great blue horse to Maeve's house. He dismounted and began pounding on the door. When the farmer answered, the lad said that he had come to fetch Maeve to attend his mistress, for Maeve was well known in her country as a midwife to those born both high and low.

The farmer invited the lad in for some food, but the young man was in a great hurry and said, "No, I am to stay by my horse until we go."

Now Maeve, who was always ready to attend to any need, heard this and came outside. She said that she was ready, but that she would not go a step with the boy until he at least partook of their hospitality.

The lad said, "Did you not save the life of my mistress in the field only these few days ago? And now you will turn your back on her need?"

Then Maeve remembered the frog and realized it had been a fairy in disguise. She knew that after saving a fairy's life she was responsible for that life forevermore.

So, Maeve turned and told her husband that she must go. She climbed on the horse with the lad, but before he could lash the horse to depart, the farmer grabbed the bridle and made the lad promise he would bring his wife safely home. Then off went the great blue horse at a full gallop, Maeve holding tight for dear life itself.

In a very short time, they reached the summit of the highest hill in the county. There, the lad turned the horse to face a great chasm. When Maeve saw what he was about, she cried out, "What do you mean? Do you expect us to leap over this chasm?"

But before the words had time to hang in the air, the horse was out and over the chasm like a bird on the wing.

"Well done, blue kitten!" said the lad to his mount, and Maeve saw that not only were they on the other side of the chasm, but that it was none other than a blue house cat that had taken them over.

Stopping the cat, the lad turned to Maeve. "I am taking you to the Fairy Knoll, which lies yonder on the next hill. There you will attend the Queen of the Fairies, for it was she that was the frog you saved. But before we proceed further, let me give you some advice, for I am not a fairy at all, but only a human being like yourself, who lies under a fairy spell these past twenty years."

"Things are not as they appear there," the lad continued, "but if you do as I tell, you will not be deceived and may have the power to return home. When you arrive you will be given three kinds of soap: one white, another yellow, and the third red. Rub the white soap over your right eye and it will remove the glamour. But do not touch your eyes or your brow with either of the other kind."

"White for right," said Maeve. "That's easy enough to remember."

But the lad only frowned, for he well knew the fairies' magic. "Take heed what you say and do among the fairies," he said. "Here is my second advice. When I come to take you back, the fairies will gather around you, each with some gift. Take nothing made of gold or silver. When the time comes, I will tell you what to do with the other gifts. Do you understand?"

"I believe so," said Maeve. And off they went to the Fairy Knoll.

When Maeve entered the Fairy Knoll, she found it to be a grand palace. The walls and the ceiling were lined with gold and silver, and on the floor stood a long table filled with every kind of food and drink. A great company of the most handsome lads and beautiful lasses Maeve had ever seen, all arrayed in green garments, welcomed her. Then the handsomest man took her by his hand and led her to the queen's chambers.

The queen, who was soon to give birth, rejoiced to see Maeve. "Ah, now I can get on with it for I've got my midwife with me," she said, and soon indeed a new fairy princess was born. Then all the fairies, and especially the queen, pleaded with Maeve to stay with

Land and sea in County Kerry

them but awhile. As the food and company were to her liking, Maeve agreed. Then they gave Maeve her own green garments and great jewelry laden with precious stones and three kinds of soap—red, yellow, and white. And Maeve remembered some of what the lad had told her and did not use the soap. But she did not even use the white soap, for she could not recall which soap was good and which was bad, so strong was the magic inside the Fairy Knoll.

One day when she found herself alone, Maeve looked in a mirror and found that she had become pretty—in fact, beautiful. Now growing more comely would no doubt please most of us, but Maeve had a keener mind, and she recalled the lad's words that things were not as they appeared in the Fairy Knoll.

So Maeve sat and thought until her mind cleared enough to remember a simple rhyme—"white for right." She took the white soap and rubbed it over her right eye. Suddenly, everything around her was changed.

The grand palace of the Fairy Knoll was turned into a pit of red gravel, and the long table with the fine food and drink was really an old plank with only a few old cabbage heads and green turnips strewn about.

When the fairies returned from their revels, Maeve saw them as they were, too. The tall, handsome people she had called friends were really small, ill-formed creatures. And the queen's great royal beauty was now replaced with cracked skin and merely a few threads of white hair left upon her head.

Maeve bowed before the queen and told her that she missed her husband. “Sure, my heart’s about to break in two if I don’t see him again,” Maeve said, not letting on that she could now see the fairies for what they were.

The queen was suspicious and questioned Maeve closely, asking her if she would take another bite of the light white cake, which was really a rotting potato, or have a sip of the delightful mead, which Maeve could clearly see was nothing more than water from a ditch. But she refused none of it and even danced a last dance with the handsome man who first led her to the queen’s chamber, only he was really an old yellow frog covered with warts.

When the queen believed that Maeve’s heart was set on seeing her husband again, she called the lad to take her for one last visit. When she was ready to go, the fairies all gathered around, each with a token of their goodwill, just as the lad had predicted. Maeve’s head was clear, and she remembered to refuse anything with gold and silver. But she did take everything else that was offered.

Then she was placed again on the blue cat, and they departed. But the lad took a new road home, one that led through a patch of briar and thornbushes. As soon as they reached the first bush, the lad said, “Throw one of the fairy gifts into the bush.”

Maeve did as he said and threw a scarf into the bush. Once it hit the bush, the scarf exploded as loud as a cannon shot and turned the bush into a ball of fire. As they rode on, Maeve did the same with the rest of her gifts. One after another, each one exploded into flame.

When they were through the briars and thorns, the lad said, "If you had kept those things and carried them home, they would have set your house on fire and burnt your house and husband to the ground, so that you had no home to return to."

But as it was, they reached her home in safety. When Maeve got down from the blue cat, her husband rushed out to greet her. In their embrace they did not notice the lad's departure on his great blue horse, headed again in the direction of the Fairy Knoll.

Tom Moore and the Silky

In the fishing village of Inch, on the far-off Dingle Peninsula, there once lived a fine, brave, young fisherman named Tom Moore. Tom was renowned as a dancer and singer, often singing in his curragh, a typical small boat of the region, or dancing about the cliffs at night.

Now both Tom's mother and father had died when he was but a lad, and he had been alone in his father's house for many years, when he decided it was time to take a wife. One morning, as he was working the nets near an island, the finest woman he'd ever seen appeared lying on a rock, fast asleep.

Now the tide had gone from the rocks, and Tom wanted to know who the young lady was and how she had come to be sleeping upon the rocks. So he rowed over and shouted, "Wake up! Wake up! If the tide comes up, you'll be drowned."

The woman raised her head and only laughed at Tom. Tom was insulted and was going to leave the woman to her own devices, but every time he turned to look at her she was more beautiful than before. He found that he couldn't even do his work, he was so compelled to look at the beautiful woman.

The tide was coming on fast, and Tom saw that it would soon cover the rock, so he rowed back out to the woman. But before he got there, she threw back her long black hair and slipped into the sea.

Tom could work no more, and so he spent the rest of the day cursing himself for not taking the woman from the rock. "Sure, it was God himself that sent her to me," he muttered, "and I have thrown her back to the sea."

He went home, but he could neither eat nor sing nor dance. In fact, he didn't sleep a nod throughout the night, and the dawn's first light found him out at the rock again. And again the beautiful woman was there.

Brandon Bay, on the Dingle Peninsula

This time he called to her gently, not rudely like the first time.

"Hullo, there," said Tom. "It's a fine, gentle morning now."

But the woman did not answer Tom, and she hid her face from view with the hood of her lustrous cloak.

"Now you don't want to be staying out here again and spending another night in the water," Tom entreated. But still the woman would not answer.

He rowed next to the rock and pleaded, "You may as well come home with me, you know." Not a word from the woman.

"Well, at least I'll have this," he said and grabbed the woman's black hood.

"Give me back my hood, Tom Moore," the woman suddenly cried.

"Indeed, I will not," said Tom, "for it was God that sent you and, now that you have speech, I'm well satisfied." Saying this, he stepped on the rock, took her by the hand, and led her to his boat. She said nothing, but came without protest.

When they got back to Tom's house, he fixed a breakfast of tea and bread and sat down next to the woman. "Now, seeing as people around here like to talk, in the name of God, you and I will go to the priest and get married today. That'll put a stop to some of the talking anyway."

So they went to the priest and got married. And the woman was as good a wife as ever in a man's house.

Now she lived with Tom seven years and, in that time, they had three sons and two daughters. One day, Tom was working on his boat when some of the rigging broke. He thought there were some bolts in the loft, so he went to look for them. Now he was in a haste to find the bolts, for the mackerel were running, and he threw down all kinds of ropes and bags trying to find them.

And what should also come down but the hood he'd taken from his wife that morning seven years ago. She saw it the moment it fell, so she gently picked it up from the floor and hid it behind her back. Then a great seal began to roar loudly from the beach.

"Ah, that'll be my first husband looking for me," said Tom's wife, but Tom paid no attention and went to fix his boat. All that night the great seal roared from the beach, and the people of Inch said, "He's mourning for his wife."

The next day, when Tom was out fishing for the mackerel, his wife swept the house clean, put every pot and teacup in order, and even combed the children's hair. Then, taking them one by one, she kissed them each on the mouth. Then she went to the beach, put the hood on her head, and plunged into the sea.

At that moment, the great seal roared so loudly, he could be heard ten miles away. And soon the fishermen saw him swimming in the current with a beautiful black seal by his side.

Now when Tom came back, the children told him what his wife had done, and he knew she had gone back to her people, for he had always known she was a silky, one of the strange creatures who lead half their life at sea and half with the folks on land.

Of course, Tom had his three sons and two daughters, and they all had webbed fingers and toes to remind him of his seven happy years with the silky. And, to this day, such remnants can be found on the Moores of Inch in Dingle, although the webbing shrinks with every generation.

Enchanted Crickets

Since crickets are believed to be enchanted, people do not like to speak ill of them. So these tiny insects are spoken of with great mystery and awe. No one would venture to kill them or do them any harm.

Crickets are by no means evil. On the contrary, the presence of the cricket is considered lucky. Their singing keeps away the fairies at night, who are always anxious in their selfish way to have the whole hearth kept clear for themselves. They want to quietly sit 'round the last embers of the fire and peacefully sip the cup of milk left for them by the farmer's wife. The crickets will chirp and chatter the night away, making certain that the house is not overrun by the partying wee folk who stay past their welcome.

The crickets are supposed to be hundreds of years old. Consequently, if we could understand their talk, it would no doubt be interesting and instructive.

Jack and His Three Friends

Once there was a poor widow, and she had one son named Jack. Now summer came before the new potatoes and found Jack and his mother even poorer than before. So Jack said to his mother, "Bake my cake and kill my cock, for I am off to seek my fortune, and if I find it I'll soon be back to share it with you."

So she did as he asked. On the day Jack was to leave, his mother came as far as the gate and said, "Jack, would you rather have half the cake and half the cock with my blessing, or all of them with my curse?"

"Ah, mother," said Jack, "sure you know I wouldn't have your curse. You may keep half, and welcome to it."

Jack's mother then gave him a kiss and said, "That's my boy. Here's the whole lot to you and my thousand blessings with them." As Jack walked down the lane, his mother watched 'til he was out of her sight, blessing him as far as her eyes could see.

Well, Jack went along, but never found a farmer who wanted a hand in the field or a servant in the house. The road led beside a bog, and there Jack found a poor donkey up to his shoulders in the mud. "Ah, Jack, ashore there," cried the donkey. "Lend us a hand or I'll be drowned."

"Never ask twice," said Jack. He threw big stones and pieces of sod into the bog until the donkey got his feet under him. "Thank you, Jack. I'll do as much for you another time," said the donkey. "Where are you off to?"

"To seek my fortune," said Jack, "and you may come along if you wish."

"Aye, I think I will," said the donkey. "Who knows what luck we may have!"

In the next village they entered, they saw a group of mean young boys chasing after a poor dog with a cup tied to its tail. Upon seeing Jack, the dog ran to him for protection, for Jack had the look of a kindly man. Then the donkey roared and kicked its legs up in the air, and the little scoundrels took to their heels.

"More power to you, Jack," said the dog, panting from his troubles, "and much obliged to you, Mr. Donkey, too. Whither is it you are traveling?"

"To seek our fortune," said Jack, "and you may join us if you wish."

"I would be proud to go with you," said the dog.

So the three friends left the village and its rowdy boys. Not far from town, they decided to have their lunch, Jack sharing his cake and cock with the dog, and the donkey helping himself to some thistles. While they were eating and talking, what should come by but a poor, half-starved cat. Again, Jack took pity on a helpless creature and said, "You look as if you've seen the last of your nine lives, friend. Here, take this bone and some cake."

The cat eagerly devoured the food. After he had finished licking himself clean, he said to Jack, "May your family never know a hungry belly. And may I be so bold as to inquire where you're going?"

"To seek our fortune," said Jack, "and we'd be happy if you'd join us."

Off marched the four friends to find their fortune, but having not found it by nightfall, they decided to look for a place to sleep. Since neither castle nor cottage was near, Jack said, "Well, we'll have the worse luck now and the better another time—and, after all, it's a warm summer's night."

So they went into the woods and made beds on the long grass in the clearing. But no sooner had they fallen asleep than they heard laughter and singing and other wild sounds nearby. Mounting the tallest tree with ease, the cat spied the glow of candlelight not far off.

"Since we're already awake," said Jack, "we might as well go see if they'll kindly give us lodgings."

But as they approached the crude cabin out of which the sounds erupted, Jack grew cautious. "On tippytoes, boys," he told his friends, "until we see what sort of people make such a racket in the middle of the night."

So they crept to a window, and the dog sat on the donkey, and the cat sat on the dog so that all could see in. And what did they see but six robbers, with pistols and drawn swords, drinking mulled wine and eating roast beef. Before them on the table stood a pile of gold and silver.

"Wasn't that a fine haul we took from Lord Dunlavin," said the ugliest thief, who looked like the head of the gang.

Upon hearing this, Jack said, "Close your ranks, comrades. Let each of you mind my word of command." Then Jack made a sign and they all commenced to sing out like mad. The donkey roared, "Hee-haw! Hee-haw!" The dog barked, "Bow-wow!" The cat screeched, "Meow! Meow!" And good Jack yelled, "Level your pistols, men, and let fly! Don't leave one of them alive!" Then the donkey smashed every pane in the window with his hooves.

The robbers were frightened for their lives and began to yell that the devil himself was about. They knocked over the candles, bumped into each other trying to get out the door, and ran into the woods, never looking back. Who knows, they may be running still!

So Jack and his three friends went into the cabin, closed the door and the shutters, lit the candles, and ate and drank their fill. Then they slept soundly, Jack in the bed, the donkey in the stable, the dog on the doormat, and the cat by the fire.

The next morning, they ate a hearty breakfast and gathered up Lord Dunlavin's treasure in a bag, for they had all agreed to travel to Dunlavin Castle to return his gold and silver. Now the castle was not far, for robbers are too lazy to travel for their plunder. By midday, they were at the castle gates.

Jack knocked on the gates, and a stern-looking guard opened the portal. "Who are you, and what do you want?" he demanded.

"I'm Jack, and these are my friends. We are seeking our fortune, and we found it this morning," said Jack, opening the bag to reveal the gold and silver. Seeing the riches that Jack displayed, the guard was only too happy to let Jack into the castle. Once inside, Jack asked to see Lord Dunlavin himself.

The guard frowned. "I suppose it would be all right for yourself, sir," he said, "but I must draw the line at letting animals in to see the lord."

"But this is Tom, the King of the Cats before you. And do you not recognize Bran, Finn McCool's own hound?" said Jack. And taking the guard aside he whispered,

Near Innishannon in County Cork

"And this poor donkey here is none other than the Prince of the Realm under some fairy magic. Why they've all got more right to see the lord than you or I."

The guard was so impressed with the royalty before him, he went at once to announce them to the lord. And wasn't Lord Dunlavin surprised when in strutted Jack, the cat, the dog, and the donkey after they'd been announced as Jack, a wealthy merchant, King Tom, Bran of the Fenians, and The Prince of the Realm.

But the lord's surprise turned to happy shouts of joy when Jack laid out all the gold and silver that had been stolen the night before.

"Here is all your gold and silver returned home," said Jack. "Now I hope you won't begrudge us our supper and a bed until we may resume our travels."

"Your travels?" said the king. "Where are you going?"

"To seek our fortunes," said Jack.

"Then you may stop your search here," said the lord, "for not one of you will ever see a poor day from this moment on if I can help it."

So all were welcomed at Dunlavin Castle and all received their heart's content. The donkey and the dog got the best posts in the farmyard and the choicest scraps from dinner. The cat took possession of the kitchen and warmed himself by the fire every night.

As for Jack, he kept his promise to his mother and brought her to the castle to live in comfort. Lord Dunlavin made Jack his steward, for everyone said Jack had the air of a born gentleman. And you won't be surprised to find that Jack married the lord's daughter in only a few years and eventually became a lord himself. His first act was the knighting of Sir Cat, Sir Dog, and Sir Donkey.

Not Quite Natural Causes

Local Irish courts offer some of the most endearing and bizarre stories to come out of the Emerald Isle. Here is one such story:

Once, a farmer sued the local authorities for destroying his cow because of the suspicion that the animal had rabies. If the cow had been killed only upon a suspicion of illness, then the farmer would be paid. But if the cow was proved to have been rabid before its destruction, then no payment would be given. The proof usually required a microscopic examination of the spinal cord. However, in this case, no such examination had been performed.

Cattle grazing near a stream in Ireland

The defense appeared hopeless. But the authorities produced their own doctor who swore, "That cow had rabies by the infallible test."

"What test did you apply?" asked the magistrate.

"I brought a dog into the stall with the cow, and the cow began to bark—that's the only infallible test."

The judge doubted the doctor's medical ability and asked, "Was that the only symptom you noticed in this case?"

The doctor did not hesitate. "No, in this case, there was the sudden death of the cow."

"Hmmm," said the judge. "Did she die very suddenly?"

"Very suddenly," said the doctor.

"Describe what happened," said the judge.

"I shot her," said the doctor.

The Last of the Fairies' Royal Steeds

Of the great breed of splendid fairy horses reared by the Tuatha de Danann, some remained living for several centuries after Ireland was Christianized. These noble beasts were known by their magnificent shape and racing quality. The last of them belonged to a great lord in Connaught.

When this nobleman finally died, all his possessions were sold at auction. Included among the priceless objects from the lord's estate was the horse.

The steed was purchased by an emissary of the English government, who wanted a specimen to be transported to England. However, only those born of

Irish royal blood could ride the high-spirited animal. So when the English groom attempted to mount the fairy creature, the great horse reared and thrust out its front hooves, smashing the side of his stall. He threw the base-born churl violently to the ground, killing him on the spot.

Then, fleet as the wind, the horse leapt over the heads of the throng at the auction and galloped away. It thundered across bogland and wheat field, over high mountains and through deep valleys in its whirlwind rush. With nary a drop of foam misplaced, the horse finally plunged into a lake and was seen no more. So ended the great race of the Tuatha dé Danann horses, the likes of which have never been seen again.

The Children of Lir

King Lir was never able to be happy. His first loving wife died, so he sought relief by traveling, hoping to place her memory behind him. On a visit to the King of Connacht, Lir was smitten with love again. This time it was with the beautiful and virtuous Princess Aebh, who became his new wife. She bore him twins: Fionula and Aodh. In a second birth, there were other twins: Fiachra and Conn. But this brought about his new wife's death, and Lir was devastated again.

He was tempted to try marriage once more, feeling that the children needed a mother to help raise them. In his sorrow, he again visited the court of his father-in-law. There he met Princess Aoifé, sister of Aebh, and hoped that she might consent to be his third wife. She did.

For a year, they were a loving couple. But soon thereafter, Aoifé grew increasingly jealous of the attention Lir paid to his children. A wicked druid passing by heard Aoifé's complaints and offered a terrible suggestion: the youngsters must be removed from her home.

"Come, children. We will visit your grandfather," she said, taking the druid's advice. Aoifé commanded her maids to bundle up the youngsters and prepare them for the journey. Little did the children know what was awaiting them! As for herself, Aoifé put on her very best clothing and jewels. When all was prepared, the family set out for her father's castle near Loch Derravaragh, in today's County Westmeath, where it commanded a wide view. On the way, Aoifé tried to convince her charioteer to kill the children, but he would not. She knew she had to do the deed herself. On the ride, she formed a plan.

Young Fionula did not trust her stepmother and, thus, watched her every move. When they arrived at the lake, the older woman ordered the children to bathe themselves. But Fionula and the others refused. However, Aoifé and her handmaidens forced them into the water. There, by a touch to the head with a wand provided by the evil druid, she changed each child into a beautiful swan.

"Thus you will remain until men with shaved heads come to these shores and set up their tables at the east end of this lake. There, they will ring their bells. Until then, you will stay as swans, traveling so as never to have a home again. Now be gone out to the lake. I am through with you, and now I will have my husband, your father, to myself."

When Aoifé arrived at her father's fortress, the King of Connacht asked about his grandchildren. He did not believe his daughter's story about them being at home. A powerful magician himself, the king cast his daughter into a deep sleep and coaxed her to talk about what she had done. Awakening her, the king scolded her mightily for her evil ways. In the presence of the court, he changed her into a gray vulture with a wave of his hand. The wicked woman was condemned to live forever in the world's roaring wind and hail, never to have any comfort of the hearth again.

All the king's attendants rushed to the lakeside to find the children, but everyone was enchanted by powerful magic once they arrived. The court spent its time frolicking and listening to the wonderful music of the birds. The chariots stood empty on the shore, and the horses went hungry. Day and night, the warriors and their ladies stood entranced, since the magic of Aoifé remained so strong. Through the warmth of the summer and on to the winter, they all remained under the spell. Many of them were also changed into birds, and they can still be seen returning to the shores of Loch Derravaragh every spring. Lir, the father, died far away of heartbreak.

Three hundred years went by, with Fionula sheltering the shivering swan children under her spreading wings through rain, snow, and sleet. Finally, they flew out to the Sea of Moyle between Erinn and Alba, where they remained under their stepmother's spell for another three hundred years.

In their flight, the swan children passed over the fields where they had played centuries ago as real people. But now all was gone of their home, which had collapsed under the wind and storms of the ages.

The swan children endured yet another three hundred years of their sad condition, this time on the raging waters of the great western sea near Erris. But one bright spring midday, they returned to the shores of glittering Loch Derravaragh, where monks were praying. A monastery had been built there years before on the eastern end of the far water. As the swan children swam by, the church bells rang for daily prayers. With that joyous sound, they immediately regained their human form. The children were baptized by the astounded monks, and that renewed their happy souls forever.

Pointing to Eternity

A Clareman fond of hunting was proud of the new setter he had just purchased. The dog had come from the purest stock and was rumored to be almost magical in its ability to find game and stay on point. It was a grand dog, everyone agreed. As the talk progressed, the expected qualities of the animal grew and grew.

As soon as the weather permitted, the man invited his neighbors on a hunt with his new setter in order to show off the dog's marvelous talents. As the group trod out to the wild, windblown cliffs of Clare, the dog suddenly disappeared into the brush. It was close to the end of spring, and the leaves were full and green.

No one could see the dog and, call as he might, the worried owner could not get the setter to come. The man and many of his friends searched all day but could not find the dog. Finally, his friends persuaded the man that the dog, unfamiliar with the lay of the land, had gotten lost and fallen off a steep cliff into the raging sea. The man was distraught, for not only had he lost a fine hunting dog, he also felt like a fool.

Summer passed, the dog was forgotten, and the cold breezes of autumn blew off the leaves from the bushes. Soon the man was out on the cliffs again, dreaming of the next year's hunt.

As he was strolling along, he came upon the spot where the setter had disappeared. In the tangle of the brush, now bereft of its leafy cover, the man saw two skeletons. One was the setter, still in a perfect set, his tail bones erect, and his nose bone pointed deeper into the brush. For that is where the skeleton of a pheasant stood, still frozen, evading the hunters.

A scenic view in Connemara

Photo credits:
Front cover: **John P. Stevens/Ancient Art & Architecture Collection LTD.** (center); **David Wenzel** (border).

Ancient Art & Architecture Collection LTD.: Ronald Sheridan: 156; Robert Smith: 148; John P. Stevens: 5, 182; **Bridgeman Art Library, London/New York:** *The Overture*, by Edwin Thomas Roberts, Christie's Images, London: 63; "*The Fairy Dance*" (early 20th-century illustration), Private Collection: 53; **Corbis:** Dallas & John Heaton: 32; Warren Morgan: 64; C. Philip: 39; Mike Yamashita: 83, 105; **E.T. Archive:** 219; **Mary Evans Picture Library:** 15, 97; **FPG International:** Bruce Byers: 189; Dennie Cody: 153; Michael Hart: 37; Richard Laird: 131; Mike Malyszko: 212; Guy Marche: 150; Michael Nelson; 199; Martin Rogers: 92; Telegraph Colour Library: 85; Travelpix: 108, 161, 177; **Image Bank/Chicago:** Alan Becker: 231; Wendy Chan: 168; Mahaux Photography: 163; **Image Select:** 51, 88, 117; Chris Fairclough: 22, 56, 122, 248; **International Stock:** Robert Beckhard: 224; Joe Budde: 79; J.G. Edmanson: 119, 255; Chad Ehlers: 101; Chris Warren: 113; Hilary Wilkes: 99, 142, 221, 236; **SuperStock:** 4, 7, 11, 34, 42, 47, 74, 135, 139, 245; **David Wenzel:** (interior border).